David N. Blondell

5/7/73

SEX WITHOUT FEAR

"YE SHALL KNOW **THE** TRUTH, AND THE TRUTH SHALL MAKE YOU FREE."

JOHN viii, 32

S. A. LEWIN, M.D. and JOHN GILMORE, Ph.D.

SEX WITHOUT FEAR

Foreword by

SARAH K. GREENBERG, M.D.

THIRD REVISED EDITION

by

NORMAN APPLEZWEIG, M.S.

MEDICAL RESEARCH PRESS

DEDICATED TO THE MARRIED AND THOSE ABOUT TO BE

A NOTE ABOUT THE AUTHORS

S. A. LEWIN, M.D. is the author of *Health and Hygiene*. He was formerly Chief of the Bureau of Preventable Diseases, Boro of Richmond, N. Y. A former Field Director of Syphilis Detection Survey, he has been a contributor to leading medical journals, a lecturer and a general practitioner for over forty years.

JOHN GILMORE, PH.D. is an internationally known medical artist. He is the illustrator of *Sterility, Sex Endocrinology, Experimental Syphilis,* and many others. He was art director of the Venereal Disease Exhibit at the Century of Progress Exposition. The former art editor of *Clinical Symposia,* he is a contributing author and artist to scientific and lay journals in the field of medicine.

SARAH K. GREENBERG, M.D. is the author of *Facts and Frauds in Women's Hygiene.* She is Associate Gynecologist and Obstetrician at the Jewish Hospital and the Kingston Avenue Hospital in Brooklyn, New York.

NORMAN APPLEZWEIG, Consulting Biochemist, specializing in hormone chemistry and physiology, is lecturer in Pharmacology at the New York Medical College and consultant to the New York Fertility Institute.

CONTENTS

LIST OF ILLUSTRATIONS

Foreword: The sex function and the reproductive process are older than man. They are basic factors common to all people, everywhere, yet a heavy veil of superstition and misinformation has been drawn for centuries over everything pertaining to sex, reproduction and marital relations in general.

In my forty years of active practice I have seen the heavy price paid for the "luxury" of ignorance. Unhappy marriages, maladjusted children, desperate, bitter, frustrated lives, all suffering because of the lack of proper sex education. The number of divorces is appalling; the staggering totals climb higher every year. And head and shoulders over every other cause is "incompatibility" Divorces mean broken homes and uprooted, insecure children who will, in turn, grow up unfit for marriage.

Today, the American people are trying to break out of this vicious circle. They are tired of evasions and ignorance. There is a strong desire to learn the truth about sex and its place in our lives. The revelations of the Kinsey report proved the deep need there is for sound sex education. The people are beginning to do something about it. Lecture and discussion groups are springing up; parent-teacher groups study the problem; there is even a recent excellent film on sex education for school children. And, of course, a great deal has been written on the subject.

In my opinion, one of the best books in the field is this new one, you are now reading. What makes it especially valuable is its simplicity and clarity. It is easy for anyone to read and understand it. In simple, everyday language, avoiding technical or obscure phraseology, the authors present medically, psychologically and ethically correct information. The book is not padded with extraneous material, but pursues one clear line.

Unique and vital are the illustrations. *Sex Without Fear* is the only fully illustrated book on the subject. Dr. Gilmore's beautiful drawings carry the text along, highlighting it at every point with an artistry at once clear, precise and esthetically enjoyable.

This excellent volume also boasts a glossary, and the authors may well be proud of its inclusion. Physicians know only too well the difficulties many patients encounter in attempting to detail their ailments, with the limited and usually coarse vocabulary learned from school lavatory walls and street-corner gatherings. Ignorance of proper terminology has deterred many couples from talking over their problems and has been a definite factor in the failure of many parents to give their children some sex education.

Another pleasant factor is the low price of the book, which makes it available to the greatest number of people.

It is my personal belief that the authors have made a vital contribution to the emotional health and psychological balance of every young couple who are starting out to establish their own family units.

SARAH K. GREENBERG, M.D.

Introduction: At present, one of every three marriages ends in the divorce court. This proves that *education,* not marriage has failed. Dr. Paul Papenoe reports that where couples merely consult the Institute of Family Relations, Los Angeles, hardly one marriage in 5000 has failed; organized education could do even better. Whether it is called incompatibility or mental cruelty or infidelity or any other such broad term, basically it is failure to achieve satisfactory marital relations that is the cause of the vast majority of divorces.

Sexual adjustment in marriage is the deepest concern of every man and woman. Yet such is the inadequacy of sex education that confusion and superstition cloud the minds of most people today. It is not that people do not seek to learn the true facts about sex, but that so little is offered them.

The lack of sex education in American schools and colleges is appalling. Nor are medical schools much farther advanced in the teaching of sex education and sex practices. In "Sexual Behavior In The Human Male", Dr. Alfred C. Kinsey demonstrates how inadequate knowledge affects our lives, our laws and our relations with each other. A pertinent example is the large number of men who know nothing about female anatomy or sex functions and therefore do not know how to act effectively in sex relations.

Women, because of the restraints of their upbringing, possess even less knowledge and understanding of men. The results of so much ignorance can only be disastrous to society and the individuals who make up society.

15

There have been many excellent books written on the subject of sex and marriage. Unfortunately, however, a great many of them are written in language easily understood only by people with a college education or a medical degree.

The authors have become increasingly aware of the anxiety on the part of most young couples to build their married life on a firm foundation. They have been besieged with questions; led into endless discussions; pursued with requests for "a book I can understand", "something clear but simple", etc. After a careful survey of the available literature, they decided to prepare this volume, couched in layman's terms, fully illustrated with simple, yet medically correct illustrations, with a comprehensive glossary and at a modest price, yet covering every necessary aspect of sex and sex relationships.

This book is addressed primarily to the young couple just starting married life. To them, the authors say: study yourself and your partner. Learn how your bodies function. Learn what causes you pleasure and how to give pleasure to each other. Above all else, be frank and open with each other. Discuss the most intimate details freely and honestly. Don't let false modesty or foolish shame cause misunderstanding, doubt and worry. Marriage must be worked at, to be successful, but if approached with common sense and loving tenderness, it will yield profits beyond your dreams.

The authors wish to express their gratitude to F. K. Lewin, for her painstaking research, deft co-ordination of material and invaluable editorial assistance.

CHAPTER ONE

THE REPRODUCTIVE SYSTEM

"Male and Female Created He Them"

GENESIS *Chapter 1 Verse 27*

Every couple should have a clear understanding of both male and female anatomy, the difference in their functions and the role each plays in reproduction. Man and woman are equal partners, each dependent on the other and unable to function sexualy alone. Following is a brief description of the reproductive system:

The female reproductive system

The organs that make up the female generative system are, internally, ovaries, fallopian tubes, uterus (womb), and vagina. The external genitals are called collectively the "vulva", and consist of the larger lips (labia majora), lesser lips (labia minora), the clitoris and the openings of the vagina and urethra.

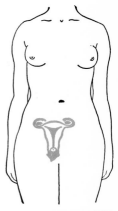

The ovaries, two small glands about the size of plumbs, are located in the lower part of the adbomen, one on each side, near the upper end of the uterus. They are between one and one and one-half inches long and about one-half inch thick. Once during each month, or menstrual cycle, one of the ovaries releases an egg or ovum, which is sucked into the fallopian tube. This process is called ovulation. The egg proceeds along the tube to the uterus. If it is not fertilized in the fallopian tube, it disintegrates in the uterus. If intercourse has taken place preceding ovulation and contraceptive measures have

THE FEMALE REPRODUCTIVE
SYSTEM

ures have not been utilized, the egg cell will be fertilized in the fallopian tube and, upon reaching the uterus, will attach itself to the lining and begin to develop.

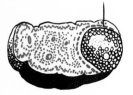

GRAAFIAN FOLLICLE

CROSS-SECTION OF OVARY

In addition to producing eggs, the ovaries secrete chemical substances called hormones. These will be discussed in the chapter on the endocrine glands.

The fallopian tubes, which carry the egg from the ovary, are connected to the upper part of the uterus and open into it. The end nearest the ovary has a series of small, funnel-like openings, which suck in the egg. The whole tube is about four inches long, round, and as thick as a pencil. The egg, which is almost microscopic in size, passes down into the uterus, while active sperm pass upward, to meet and impregnate the egg.

CORPUS LUTEUM

CROSS-SECTION OF OVARY

The uterus, or womb, is roughly pear shaped, with the small end down, opening into the vagina. It is a hollow, muscular organ with thick walls, lying behind the bladder and with the upper end tipped slightly forward over it. It is about three inches long, two inches wide and one inch thick. During pregnancy, it stretches to about eight inches long, and becomes oval in shape. The inch or less that extends into the vagina is called the cervix. It is shaped like a rounded cone, with a small opening in the middle. Normally, it is closed with a plug of mucus that is receptive to sperm but not to infection.

The vagina is the passage leading from the external genitals to the uterus. It is a ridged canal about three to three and one-half inches long, but extremely elastic and capable of stretching both in length and diameter. The vagina is designed for a four-fold purpose. It receives the penis in intercourse, acts as a receptacle for the semen, provides a passage for the baby at birth and for the menstrual flow.

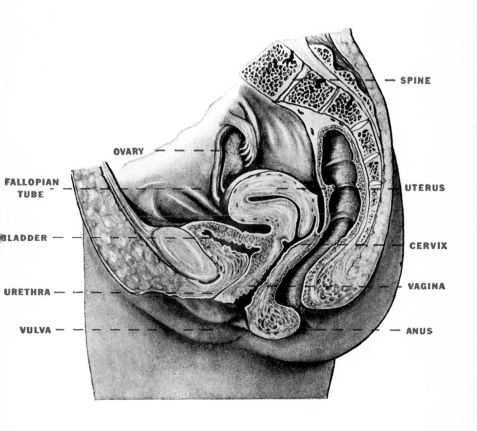

SPINE

OVARY

FALLOPIAN
TUBE

BLADDER

URETHRA

VULVA

UTERUS

CERVIX

VAGINA

ANUS

CROSS-SECTION OF FEMALE PELVIC ANATOMY

Of the external organs the only ones usually visible are the labia majora, or larger lips, thick, rounded folds of skin, covered with hair. Usually, especially in young girls, the lips are in contact with each other, and cover and protect the delicate, sensitive parts beneath. The larger lips are considered the female counterpart of the male scrotum.

Inside the area covered by the labia majora are the lesser lips, a pair of smaller, narrow folds. The lesser lips decrease in size as they go back, finally blending into the larger lips. At the front, they come together in a sort of peak, called the prepuce, covering the clitoris, the center of sensation in woman, corresponding to the head of the penis, the glans of the male. The function of the lesser lips is to guide the penis into the vagina.

The clitoris is, of course, much smaller than the penis. It varies greatly in size, from as small as one-fifth of an inch to as long as an inch and a half. To the examining finger, the tip of the clitoris will resemble a small rounded node, extremely sensitive to the touch. Like the penis, it is composed of erectile tissue, which under sexual stimulation is suffused and distended by blood. The surface covering of the head of the clitoris is supplied with special nerve endings which are especially intended for sensory stimulation and are not found anywhere else in the female sex organs. It is in the clitoris that the sexual climax is felt, and it is by stimulating the clitoris that most women can arrive at orgasm.

The clitoris differs from the penis not only in size, but also because it does not contain any opening. A woman has no ejaculation. The opening for the urethra, or urinary tract, is between the clitoris and the vagina. The opening is usually so small as to be difficult to locate.

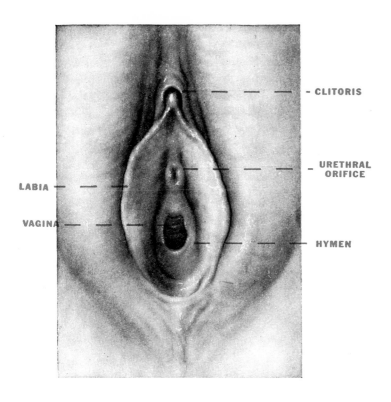

CLITORIS

URETHRAL
ORIFICE

LABIA

VAGINA

HYMEN

FRONT VIEW OF EXTERNAL FEMALE GENITALIA

Close to the opening of the vagina, on either side, lie two small glands called "Bartholin's Glands". During sexual excitement, they secrete a mucus which lubricates the entrance of the vagina. The hymen, frequently called "maidenhead", is a thin fold of tissue that partly closes the vaginal opening. Rarely does the hymen completely cover the opening. If it does, it must be opened surgically at puberty, to permit the passage of the menstrual flow. Although the hymen is usually ruptured at the first complete intercourse, it is not always so. If the vaginal opening is large, the penis small, it may not be disturbed at all. Ignorance of proper methods of intercourse, may tend to preserve a small hymen. Many a physician has been forced to open a hymen to properly conduct a pre-natal examination.

Menstruation

The menstrual cycle starts in the middle of a woman's "month", while menstruation actually occurs in the middle of the cycle. It begins when the ovary throws out an egg, which is sucked into the fallopian tube. It takes nearly two weeks to work down to the uterus, which is preparing to receive it and to nourish it if fertilized.

The uterus swells a little, the lining, or endometrium, gets thicker, its blood supply increases and its glands secrete a special mucus, all in preparation for a fertilized egg. If the egg is not fertilized, the uterus begins to shed part of its lining, with the extra blood and mucus, along with the unfertilized egg. This bleeding phase is what is commonly called menstruation. It lasts for several days, each woman having her own schedule. The average is between three and six days, as the average cycle is between twenty-five and thirty days.

The menstrual cycle is nature's continuous preparation for pregnancy. Month after month, year after year, from puberty to menopause, the cycle repeats itself. The female body is constantly passing through important and dramatic changes, of most of which she is unconscious. These changes are designed to provide food and shelter for the development of a baby. If the egg should be fertilized, it will sink into a soft, thick bed, rich with food elements, and there go through its many fascinating changes. Should the egg not be fertilized, and most of them are not, it can not cling to the uterus, but passes out along with the materials especially created to nourish it. Whereupon, the whole process immediately starts over again.

The menstrual cycle has three distinct phases. The first is called the proliferative or pre-ovulatory phase. It starts on the first day of menstruation and lasts about two weeks. The pituitary gland, (in the head), secretes a hormone that stimulates a tiny thing in the ovary called the graafian follicle. Every graafian follicle contains an egg which is stimulated by the hormone. Usually only one follicle in one ovary ripens at a time. Under the influence of the follicle-stimulating hormone, it fills with fluid and begins to produce follicular hormone. This, in turn, works on the endometrium, or lining of the uterus. It begins to get thick, its glands start developing, etc. Meanwhile, the graafian follicle has been moving to the surface of the ovary, where it finally breaks open, or ruptures. This releases the egg into the abdominal cavity, where it is sucked up into the fallopian tube. The period during which the egg is erupted and enters the tube is known as ovulation. This usually takes place between the tenth and sixteenth day after the first day of the previous period. Ovulation marks the end of the first phase.

The second phase is called the secretory or post-ovulatory phase. This lasts, roughly, about ten days. Every woman has her own time-schedule, subject to change without notice. A new endocrine gland develops in the broken graafian follicle. A substance called a yellow body (corpus luteum) is formed, which secretes a hormone called progesterone or corpus luteum hormone. This stimulates the endometrium still more, with its blood supply increasing and glands actively secreting a special mucus. The uterus is all ready for the fertilized egg.

But menstruation is keyed to the unfertilized egg. The third phase of the cycle is the bleeding phase, or menses. By the time the unfertilized egg reaches the uterus, the corpus luteum has begun to cease production of its hormone. Within a few days, the frustrated uterus begins to

Micro-sections of Endometrium as seen under the microscope

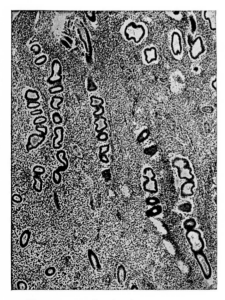 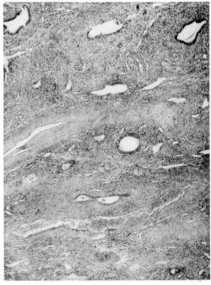

Hormone stimulated endometrium in
a young woman

Atrophic endometrium of a woman in
the post-menopause period

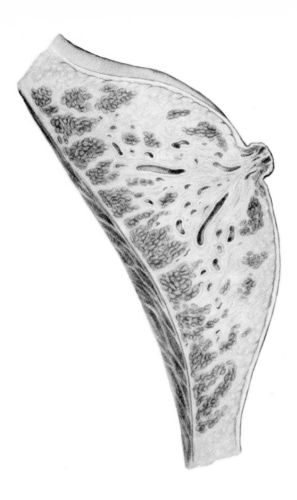

Cross-section of a Fully Developed Woman's Breast

shed its lining. Blood vessels shrink, glands become inactive. Menstruation, or bleeding, starts, to continue for from three to six days. Simultaneously, there begins again a repetition of the whole cycle.

Hygiene

Feminine daintiness is one of woman's greatest attractions. A recent popular song, Irving Berlin's "The Girl I Marry", describes the ideal girl as being soft, suggestive of maternity, beautifully dressed and sweet-smelling. Man's ideal has not changed since Solomon wrote the oldest love song in the world, "The Song of Songs": ". . . how much better is thy love than wine! and the smell of thine ointments than all spices!"

The woman who loves her husband and wants to hold his love will be careful always to look clean and smell sweet. Perfume will not take the place of soap and water, but it should not be neglected. Men are particularly susceptible to perfume. It should not be poured on, nor will a little dab behind the ears suffice. Perfume is an accent. It should be used sparingly but cleverly to provide a delightful but elusive aroma, feminine and alluring.

The daily bath is a "must". If it is impossible to take a complete bath, one can at least wash the external genitals with soap and water, also the arm-pits and any other part of the body where perspiration odor may cling.

Many women believe that it is essential to douche frequently for cleanliness. This is a mistake. Douching can destroy the protective bacteria present in the vagina. If there is an unpleasant odor from the vagina, consult a physician, who will advise on douching.

26

The male reproductive system

The male reproductive system consists of the penis, testicles, scrotum, epididymis, vas deferens, seminal vesicles, prostate gland and urethra or urinary passage.

The scrotum, which resembles a divided pouch, contains the testicles. The left side usually hangs slightly lower than the right. The scrotum changes in appearance and size depending on various factors such as temperature, etc. Normally, the testicles are found in the scrotum. They can, however, be pushed through the inguinal canal into the groin. In some cases, they remain there from birth and fail to descend at all. This condition is called undescended testicle. If both testicles fail to descend, a man will be sterile because the body temperature is too high for the development of spermatozoa. Sometimes, surgical treatment is necessary to relieve this condition, or it may be treated with hormones.

The testicles are a pair of small oval glands, about one and one-half inches long, an inch wide and less than an inch thick. Like the ovaries, they perform two functions, secretion of male sex hormones (see Endocrine Glands), and the manufacture of spermatozoa, the male seed.

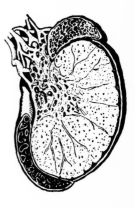

CROSS-SECTION OF TESTICLE

Inside the testicle (testis) is a series of small canals called the seminiferous tubules, in which the sperm is manufactured. The tubules come together in larger tubes called the epididymis. The sperm travels through this passage and into the vas deferens, which leads into the abdominal cavity. The vas deferens joins the seminal vesicle, which produces a secretion that causes the sperm to become active. From here, it passes through the prostate gland which adds a secretion that further stimulates the sperm. The fluid containing the spermatozoa is called semen. It is stored in the seminal vesicles and prostate gland. Under sexual excitement, it is forcefully and spasmodically ejected through the urethra. The process is called ejaculation. About one teaspoonful of semen is ejaculated at one time. It contains about one hundred million sperm. The urethra passes through the penis, with its opening in the glans, or head.

The penis is a soft, spongy organ, honey-combed with blood-vessels, which greatly increases in size when distended with blood. When relaxed, the penis is from three and one-half to four inches long and approximately one inch in diameter. When erect, it is usually between five and seven inches long and one and one-quarter to one and one-half inches in diameter. Relaxed, it hangs limply over the testicles, but erect, it curves upward and outward from the body.

The head of the penis, known as the glans, is slightly larger in diameter than the rest. It contains very sensitive nerve-endings which produce intense sensory stimulation, like in the clitoris, bringing about the climax or orgasm.

At birth, the head of the penis is covered by a narrow fold of skin called the prepuce, or foreskin. Most physicians are agreed that all boy babies should be circumcised, that is, that the foreskin should be removed. Dr. G. Lombard Kelly, Dean and Professor of Anatomy at the University of Georgia School of Medicine, has stated: "It is very unfortunate for the human race that the circumcision rite of the Hebrews did not become also a law or custom among all the races and religious cults throughout the world." As Dr. Kelly points out, the interior of the foreskin provides an incubator for the development of venereal diseases as well as accumulations

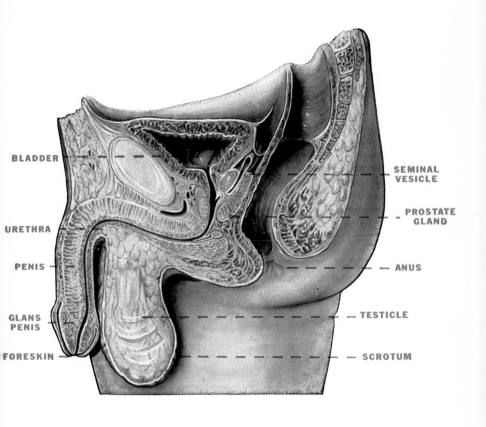

BLADDER

SEMINAL VESICLE

PROSTATE GLAND

URETHRA

PENIS

ANUS

GLANS PENIS

TESTICLE

FORESKIN

SCROTUM

CROSS-SECTION OF MALE GENITALIA

of foul-smelling secretions, known as smegma, and other infections. Also, the exposed head of the penis, after circumcision, becomes a little less sensitive, which helps to check premature ejaculation.

Hygiene

The practice of personal hygiene is extremely important to every married man. A two-day stubble or ragged fingernails will fail to attract the most devoted of wives. Body odors are almost always offensive. If it is not possible to bathe every day, the penis should be washed daily with soap and water. The foreskin of the uncircumcised male should be pulled back and the inner area thoroughly cleaned. Perspiration zones, such as the armpits, crotch and feet should be washed and powdered with a pleasantly-scented talcum. There are several toilet preparations designed for men on the market. Women are susceptible to what are considered masculine odors, tweeds and tobacco and leather and shaving lotions. Havelock Ellis has pointed out that females of all ages are even more sensitive to odors than males. Therefore, the wise husband will take pains to smell attractively.

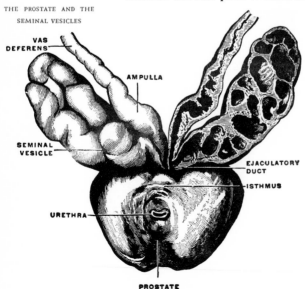

THE PROSTATE AND THE SEMINAL VESICLES

VAS DEFERENS

AMPULLA

SEMINAL VESICLE

EJACULATORY DUCT

ISTHMUS

URETHRA

PROSTATE

CHAPTER TWO

THE ENDOCRINE GLANDS

The endocrines are also known as the ductless glands or glands of internal secretion. They are the pituitary, pineal, thyroid, para-thyroid, pancreas, adrenals, ovaries and testes (testicles).

Active, functioning glands imbue the whole body and mind with a youthful vigor, self-confidence and optimism. They either control or influence such widely divergent attributes as height, ability to concentrate, color of the skin, muscular development, sexual vigor, reproduction, a woman's gracefulness and the frequency of a man's need to shave. Dr. Stone remarks that "hormones have the power of initiating and stimulating the activities of different organs and tissues. It is believed that each hormone has a specific role in the mechanism of the body. There is also considerable evidence that the various glands have a reciprocal action upon each other, and that if one does not function properly the others, too, may become affected."

The endocrine glands may be compared to minute chemical laboratories. They extract materials from the blood stream, convert them into hormones and return them to the blood which carries them, along with other materials, to every cell in the body. Each endocrine gland serves a special purpose and manufactures its own unique product.

The hormones secreted by the adrenal glands, a pair of little caps sitting astride the kidneys, are absolutely es-

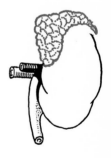

ADRENAL GLAND SITTING
ON TOP OF KIDNEY

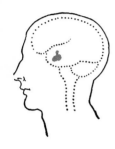

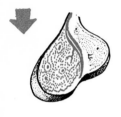

sential to life. Deficiency of the other hormones, while not fatal, results in lessened physical, mental and emotional health.

The pituitary gland, called the "Master Gland", controls the activity of all the endocrine glands. It is a small gland, about the size of an acorn, situated in the most protected spot in the whole body. It hangs under the brain, sheltered not only by the mass of brain tissue but by the roof of the mouth and the hard shell of the skull. The section of the gland called the anterior pituitary is the part that exercises influence over the other glands. In this book, we are concerned only with the action of the gonads or sex glands, the ovaries and testes.

The gonads do not, of course, function fully until maturity. But even before puberty, from earliest childhood, there is enough sex hormone being manufactured to insure marked differences between boys and girls, physically and temperamentally.

At puberty, dramatic and startling changes take place. The whole sexual network becomes active. The boy's voice "breaks", that is, deepens into masculine tones, hair sprouts on his face and body, his physical structure becomes more angular. The penis develops, erections occur, frequently accompanied by nocturnal emissions (wet dreams). The change in girls is equally great. The breasts develop, soft curves and rounded limbs replace the angular awkwardness of childhood. Hair grows in the armpits and pubic region and menstruation sets in.

The ovary secretes two hormones; the testicle, one. The female hormones are the estrogenic and corpus luteum. The male hormone is called testosterone.

The estrogenic hormone plays a vital part in the reproductive function of women as well as in their general

32   (cont. on page 38)

Location of the Endocrine Glands

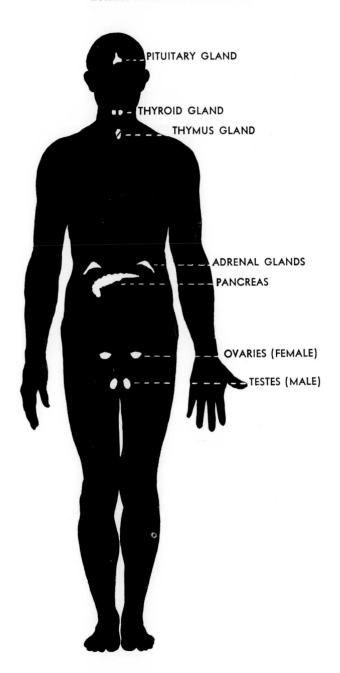

PITUITARY GLAND

THYROID GLAND

THYMUS GLAND

ADRENAL GLANDS

PANCREAS

OVARIES (FEMALE)

TESTES (MALE)

Secondary Sex Development in Man

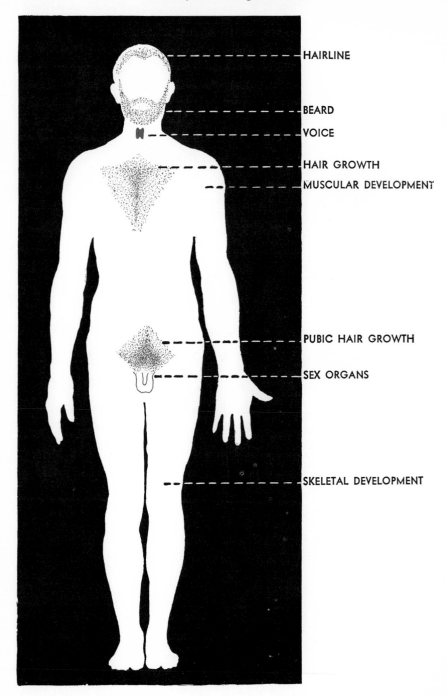

HAIRLINE

BEARD

VOICE

HAIR GROWTH

MUSCULAR DEVELOPMENT

PUBIC HAIR GROWTH

SEX ORGANS

SKELETAL DEVELOPMENT

Growth Disturbances

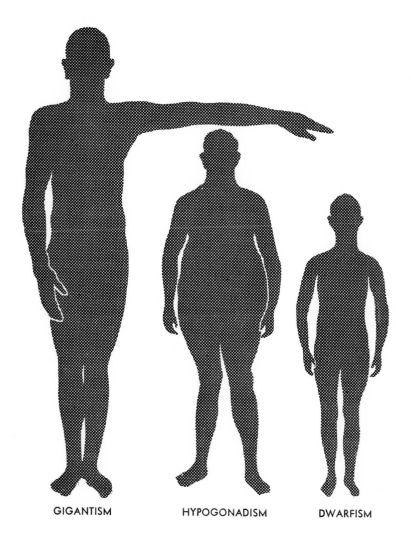

GIGANTISM   HYPOGONADISM   DWARFISM

Growth disturbances in the giant and the midget are today treated with profound and far-reaching effect with hormones. Incorrect functioning of the anterior pituitary gland is believed to be the cause of these conditions.

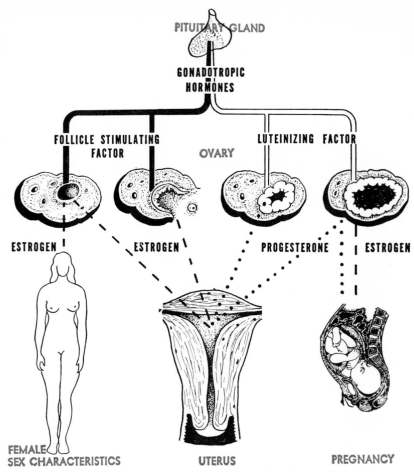

PITUITARY GLAND

GONADOTROPIC
HORMONES

FOLLICLE STIMULATING
FACTOR

OVARY

LUTEINIZING FACTOR

ESTROGEN

ESTROGEN

PROGESTERONE

ESTROGEN

FEMALE
SEX CHARACTERISTICS

UTERUS

PREGNANCY

Diagrammatic Representation of the Influence of the Female Hormones

The anterior pituitary gland secretes the gonadotropic hormones which stimulate the ovary and this in turn produces, in the first half of the menstrual cycle, the follicle-stimulating hormone, estrogen, and, in the second half, the luteinizing hormone, progesterone. During the first half of the menstrual cycle, the follicle-stimulating hormone stimulates an ovarian follicle to grow. The ovum, which is contained in the growing follicle, matures and the estrogenic hormone, estrogen, is secreted by the follicle. In the middle of the menstrual cycle, the Graafian follicle expels the ovum and then changes into the corpus luteum or yellow body. This corpus luteum is now stimulated by the luteinizing factor to excrete the other female hormone, progesterone. Both hormones, estrogen and progesterone, are essential to the normal well-functioning woman. Estrogen is essential in the development of the female sex characteristics, such as breasts, body contours, uterus, genitalia, etc. After conception, the corpus luteum, instead of regressing, becomes larger and secretes progesterone in ever-increasing amounts and maintains the pregnancy up to the third month, when the placenta takes over.

Diagrammatic Representation of the Influence of Male Hormone

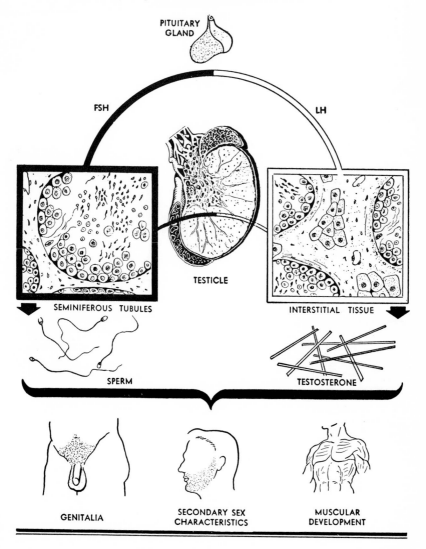

The anterior pituitary gland exerts a tremendous influence on the development of the testes. Its follicle-stimulating hormone (FSH) initiates and maintains the growth of the seminiferous tubules and the complicated development of sperm. Another pituitary product, luteinizing hormone (LH), stimulates the growth of interstitial tissue and cells which in turn secrete the male sex hormone, testosterone. Testosterone, in turn, exerts profound and widespread influence in man, being responsible for development of genitalia, secondary sex characteristics and muscular development.

well-being. Among its influences are: the first half of the menstrual cycle; size, capacity and activity of the sex organs; growth of the duct tissue of the breasts (mammary glands); secondary sex characteristics, bodily contour, distribution of fat, distribution and growth of hair, psychic attitudes. It also has an effect on woman's general constitution, her physical and mental health.

The corpus luteum hormone is directly concerned with the preparation for and maintenance of pregnancy.

The male sex hormone, testosterone, is manufactured in the tissues surrounding the seminiferous tubules in the testicle. It acts on the sex organs and on the secondary sex characteristics, such as depth of voice, distribution of hair, bone and muscle development, sexual desires, mental attitudes and traits and emotional states. It further influences the blood supply and pigmentation of the skin, muscular endurance and resistance to fatigue. It relieves irritability, apprehension, insomnia and inability to concentrate.

Laboratory-created hormones are widely used in medicine to cure a variety of ailments. Science has even found the male sex hormone invaluable for certain female diseases and vice-versa.

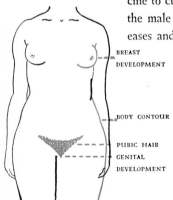

BREAST
DEVELOPMENT

BODY CONTOUR

PUBIC HAIR
GENITAL
DEVELOPMENT

Secondary Sex Characteristics in the Female

CHAPTER THREE

THE ART OF INTERCOURSE

"Therefore shall a man leave his father and his
mother, and shall cleave unto his wife: and they
shall be one flesh"

GENESIS *Chapter 2 Verse 24*

What intercourse is

Sexual intercourse (coitus) is the most intimate of personal relations. It is the blending, for one brief period, of
two bodies into one, heightened by the most ecstatic
sensations and surrounded by warmest love and deepest
trust. At least, that is what it should be. That is what it
can be when a couple understand exactly what they are
doing and the proper way to do it.

A couple marry with every intention of creating the
ideal marriage. But, too frequently, they do not know
how to adjust sexually. They go along, doing the best
they can, sometimes achieving success by accident, sometimes breaking up the marriage when sex education could
have helped to save it.

Satisfactory intercourse is the basis for happy marriage.
It does not occur automatically, but must be striven for.
It requires that each partner think first of the needs of
the other and try to attain whatever way will satisfy
those needs and give his (or her) mate happiness and
satisfaction. This will greatly heighten his own pleasure
and each will be more closely drawn to the other. There
is no room for selfishness or inconsideration in the
marriage-bed.

Physical differences place the greater burden for a

successful marriage on the husband. A man's responses are different and his reactions faster. He is easily aroused and can achieve an erection very quickly. As soon as erection occurs, he is ready for intercourse. A kiss, the sight of a nude or partly nude woman, or even the mental stimulus of thinking sexually about the woman he is with can arouse a man sufficiently for intercourse. A woman's responses are more diffused and slower to rouse. It takes a considerable amount of foreplay to arouse her completely and awaken all her responses to the proper pitch. She must be courted anew each time, caressed and petted with ever-increasing ardor until her passion is fully roused and she is ready.

Because erection comes easily and ejaculation very quickly, a man can achieve a measure of satisfaction even with an indifferent or unaroused wife. But because a woman reacts slowly, she is dependent on the man for sexual satisfaction. She needs his cooperation, his love-making. This does not mean that she should remain passive, letting him do all the wooing. Love-making must be shared. Her kiss is as intoxicating, her hands on his body as thrilling as his to her.

Then, too, the wife knows what caresses have the greatest effect on her, which actions of her husband cause the greatest pleasure. She must tell him what she needs, speaking openly and frankly. Only too often, the husband fails his wife in her greatest need. Sometimes, through selfishness and indifference, but more often through ignorance. Many men simply do not know that women, too, are capable of orgasm; in fact, should have at least one orgasm each time. Other men believe that "nice" women should be ignorant of all the techniques that make the love-play a time of delight.

Because the average woman is uneducated sexually, she may not know what is wrong, may think that intercourse is "made for men", may believe that showing pleasure in coitus would degrade her, or she may be too shy or inhibited to tell her husband frankly that something is wrong.

There must be the utmost frankness between husband and wife. This is not always easily achieved. Modesty, embarrassment, shame at bodily functions are all instilled early in life, especially in girls. It may take effort to overcome this early training, but it is necessary if the husband and wife are to reach any understanding of each other's needs and to learn to cooperate fully for mutual satisfaction.

The sex act is the highest pleasure a couple can achieve together. It is compensation for all the ills and travails of life, and meant to be shared, as the troubles are.

Courtship, or foreplay

Every act of intercourse is preceded by a period of courtship, of love-play, a building of desire and passion to the point of readiness for the final act. Some women require more love-play than others to arouse them sufficiently to take an active role in coitus, but all women require some courtship. Ellis says, "throughout the animal world courtship tends to be an art". Like other arts, it must be studied.

Although the wife should never hesitate to start the love-play when she desires to, it is usually the husband who takes the initiative, especially in the beginning of marriage. Sexually, the male is the more aggressive, the female more passive. Since a woman takes a longer time

41

to become aroused, it is up to the husband to caress and stimulate her to the desired state.

No fixed rules of courtship can be laid down. Dr. Stone makes this clear when he says, "It is neither possible nor desirable to prescribe any routine form of behavior or any set rules to be followed. In this intimate sphere of human relationship, dependence must be placed largely upon individual spontaneity and skill, as well as upon a mutual understanding and adaptation."

The erogenic zones (areas of sexual stimulation) vary in different people. In men, they are fairly localized, centering in the glans, although the ears, back of the neck, inner thighs, nipples, have varying degrees of sensitivity in different men. In women, especially early in their sexual life, the erogenic zones are more diffuse. They are not as fully aware of the centering of sensation in the genitals, and respond, sometimes even more strongly, to such erotic stimulation as nibbling the lobes of the ears, kissing and fondling of the breasts, especially the nipples, kissing and caressing of the body, generally. The building up of excitation will finally lead to caressing and stroking of the genitals, especially the clitoris. With a little practice and study, the couple will learn to know when to pass on to the next step of the act, insertion of the penis into the vagina.

Intercourse

The husband is ready for intercourse when he has a good erection. The size of the penis during erection can be increased by pressure on the dorsal vein, which runs through the middle of the upper part. This can be done by a rubber band around the base of the penis or deep penetration of the penis into the vagina, with pressure

42

of the upper part of the base of the penis against the pubic bone of the woman.

The wife's readiness is harder to determine, but can usually be expected when the secretion from the Glands of Bartholin appears and lubricates the external genitals and the entrance to the vagina. This secretion marks the wife's physical readiness. It makes entrance easier and intensifies the sexual pleasure. By this time, the entire vulva is somewhat swollen, sensitive and stiffened. The clitoris is in erection, although due to its minute size, semi-concealed position and, frequently, the fatty tissues of surrounding parts, it may not be apparent.

The act of intercourse (coitus, copulation, etc.) consists of the insertion of the erect penis into the expectant vagina and the muscular movements, many of them involuntary, leading through ever greater tension and excitation to the climax or orgasm.

During intercourse, the face and sometimes the whole body gets red. The eyes shine, the pupils are highly dilated, the blood pressure rises. Breathing becomes shallow and rapid, seeming almost to stop at times. The heart beats strong and fast. Secretions pour from the sweat glands, the Glands of Bartholin and the Glands of Cowper and Littré in the penis. There is an excess of saliva in the mouth. The muscles of the body contract involuntarily and sometimes violently. There are rhythmic contractions of the muscles at the base of the penis, expelling the semen in jets. Similar involuntary contractions, though not so violent, occur in the ring of muscles around the opening of the vagina. The climax is reached and passed and reaction sets in.

Men usually feel a sense of well-being, of satisfaction, pleasant lassitude, release from tension. In women, the reaction is similar except that they are more likely to have a sense of exhilaration, of happiness and self-assurance, an excess of energy that amounts almost to intoxication. It is usually only after prolonged or repeated coitus that a woman will feel thoroughly relaxed and tired.

The orgasm or climax

Less than one hour in one year is the very brief amount of time spent in the height of ecstasy, the orgasm. Intercourse itself takes usually from five to fifteen minutes, while the climax lasts only ten to fifteen seconds. This is quite beside the time spent in the preliminary love-play, which varies very widely. After orgasm, the feeling of tension and excitement in men fades rapidly; in women it subsides more slowly. Women are more capable of repeated orgasms than men. If a man has good control of erection, his wife can have two or more orgasms before he has his. After orgasm, the extra blood leaves the penis, it becomes flaccid and there must be a period of rest before it can become erect again. Some men are capable of only one erection at one time, while others can repeat the act several times in one session.

Orgasms vary in intensity. Some are slight while others are very strong, especially repeated orgasms, as the corpuscles are stimulated and very sensitive.

The sensation of orgasm is centered in the glans of the penis and in the clitoris. These contain a rich supply of special nerve-endings called genital corpuscles. They are the only parts of the body containing these stimulation centers. Friction of the clitoris or the glans will set off a chain reaction reaching to the sensory nerve centers of the brain and resulting in the delight of orgasm.

In men, contrary to popular belief, it is the orgasm that induces ejaculation and not the other way around. This is obvious when one remembers that young boys who masturbate do not have ejaculation but do have orgasm.

Women, who have no ejaculation, have repeated orgasms. Ejaculation is nature's method of propelling the semen from the male into the female. The female does not send seed out of her body, but retains it, and receives the male seed. Therefore, it was not necessary to provide her with ejaculatory parts. Because of the copious secretions from the Glands of Bartholin, and because there is frequently an involuntary spasmodic contraction of the muscles surrounding the opening of the vagina during orgasm, it was long believed that women did have an ejaculation of sorts. This, however, is biologically impossible.

Copulation among animals is instinctive, seasonal, based on nature's demand that each species reproduce. Intercourse between human beings is a more highly complex matter, involving as it does, psychological factors, emotions and many physical attributes. Contrary to the preachments of opponents of sex education, intercourse in man is neither "instinctive" nor "natural" unless he reduces his behavior to the bestial. The ideal to be striven for is complete satisfaction of both partners, culminating in simultaneous orgasm. This cannot be achieved without study, practice, frank and open discussion between the partners and mutual aid to achieve the desired results.

A great number of men and an amazingly large number of women are unaware that the site of sensation in the female is in the clitoris. Many women think that the climax is felt in both clitoris and vagina, and there is an old belief that the clitoris is the seat of pleasure in young girls, but after marriage, the vagina is. Although the presence of the penis in the vagina produces a feeling of pleasure and some women cannot have an orgasm unless it is there, the vagina contains no sensory nerve endings comparable to those which in the clitoris cause orgasm.

It is important that both husband and wife understand that the climax in most women is felt in the clitoris and cannot be reached without stimulation of that important organ. During intercourse, the upper part of the base of the penis should be in constant contact with the clitoris, massaging and stimulating it as it moves back and forth in the vagina. In cases where it is not possible to achieve this contact, either the man or the woman, but preferably the man, should rub the clitoris with his fingers. However, every effort should be made to devise a coital position where contact between them can be attained.

A man achieves orgasm by the friction of the rigid vaginal walls against the glans as he moves back and forth rhythmically. With a little practice, he can learn to carry on coitus for some time by pressing the base of the penis against the clitoris, making slight movements to stimulate it but not vigorously enough to further arouse his own feelings, until the woman is fully roused. She can co-operate by curtailing her own movements until the final moments.

A not uncommon source of marital unhappiness is premature ejaculation. This is when the husband cannot maintain erection and control ejaculation for even a short time after entry. Sometimes ejaculation occurs immediately upon entry, and sometimes even before, upon contact with the vulva. This is very bad for the wife, who is left in a state of tension and frustration, and bad for the husband as well. The reason may be either physical or psychological, and consultation with a physician would be wise. However, many men can train themselves to maintain erection for longer periods, with patience and the cooperation of their wives. Resting for a few moments after entry, with no coital movements until the immediate danger of ejaculation is past, is recommended. Another method to help gain control and confidence is the use of local anesthesia. Applied to the glans, it will slightly numb the nerve-endings and slow down reactions. There are several ointments suitable for the purpose, which can be obtained from a physician or druggist. A very small amount of the ointment, rubbed well into the head of the penis at least fifteen minutes before intercourse starts, should have a good effect. Care should be taken not to use too much nor start coitus too soon. A little practice will reveal the best amount and time for application. Start with only a tiny bit, no bigger than a bead. The result, in prolonged coitus and intensified climax, may well be worth the extra trouble.

Sexual lubricants

The chief lubrication for the genitals during coitus comes from the Glands of Bartholin, situated near the opening of the vagina. There are other glands high up in the vagina that lubricate that area. But there are no lubricating glands in the penis. Although some women have a great deal of secretion, others do not have enough, especially if intercourse is prolonged or repeated. It is always best to have a reliable lubricant handy.

The authors of some books purporting to give correct and scientific sex information advocate the use of saliva as being "natural". Actually, the use of saliva can be harmful! Trench mouth, or Vincent's Angina, can be

47

transmitted to the vagina, as well as several fungus infections, with serious consequences.

The best lubricators are surgical lubricating jelly and vaseline, or petrolatum. Surgical jelly is ideal because it dissolves in plain water, will not hurt rubber (diaphragm or condom), is super-smooth, stainless and greaseless. Petrolatum is heavier, greasier, needs soap and water to wash off and may stain bed-linen. But both are harmless to use, economical, and can be bought in any drug-store.

Soap lather, which is sometimes recommended, is irritating to the delicate parts and messy to use.

Frequency of intercourse

There is no hard and fast rule for frequency of intercourse. An average of twice a week seems to be the general practice, although many factors intervene. As Dr. Kelly points out, "the quality of the embrace is more important than the intervals between repetitions of it." In other words, coitus should not be practiced because "here it is Tuesday night again", but because the couple are filled with love and desire for each other. If mutual orgasm and full satisfaction are not obtained each time, there is something wrong either with the technique or the frequency.

Newly-married couples will usually have intercourse more frequently than others. People who are growing older, or those in ill-health, will practice coitus less frequently.

The important thing to remember is that there must be a satisfying climax each time. Men usually achieve this, if they are potent at all, but it is not always so with women. If a woman is not satisfied, she will, in the beginning, be ready to repeat the act sooner than if she had been satisfied, but frequent disappointment may turn her completely away from coitus altogether, as well as causing nervous complaints, insomnia, etc. On the other hand, menopause may bring heightened desire, usually because the fear of becoming pregnant is gone.

Other factors involved in frequency range from climate and diet to nervous strain, overwork and exhaustion.

Frequency must be determined by every couple for themselves. Sometimes a compromise must be reached between the partner with greater desire and the partner with less.

Indulgence below desire, for "health's sake", is unnecessary if each act of coitus is completed with satisfaction and no later ill effects, such as insomnia, tiredness, tension, a feeling of being let down generally, are felt. Sexual excesses may produce the same symptoms. One serious harm can come from coitus becoming a routine act, devoid of real interest, with consequent loss of affection. Excessive demands by one partner can kill the interest and affection of the other.

Positions for intercourse

There are supposed to be many, many positions for intercourse, known only to the initiate and promising greater delights and rarer ecstasies than the simple practices of the common people. One novelist, several years ago, described a pagan queen, with twenty-odd slits in her tunic for every possible embrace. Don't believe it. It's not true. The body can comfortably assume only a limited number of positions. And to enjoy coitus, one must be comfortable.

The traditional, or instinctive position is for the woman to lie on her back and for the man to lie on top of her.

It is not the best position but it is the most common, especially with people who lack imagination. In this position, the woman lies flat on her back, sometimes with a pillow under her hips, flexes her legs and spreads her thighs so that the man can lie between them. Complete insertion of the penis and proper contact between it and the clitoris can be easily achieved if the man does not lie too far down. The man should not lie heavily on the woman, but rest his weight on his elbows and knees. Dead weight can crush a woman painfully and destroy her pleasure and response. For prolonged coitus, he may place one or both thighs outside of hers. If she closes her thighs after entrance, it is believed that the pressure of her vulva will help a small penis maintain erection. It is possible to buy rings made of sponge rubber, which come in varying sizes, when the penis is too long for the vagina. The ring looks like a large washer and is slipped over the penis and pushed down to the base. The width of the ring controls the depth of penetration.

In many respects, the reverse, or woman-above position is the better one. Although she should be careful not to rest too heavily on the man, the woman is frequently lighter in weight. Also, and most important, she can adjust herself so that the penis is always in contact with the clitoris, and she has more freedom of movement and can abandon herself to a variety of movements that help her come to orgasm. To achieve this position, the man lies flat on his back and the woman kneels over him, astraddle, and settles down while they guide the penis into the vagina. She then straightens out her legs and lies on him, with her thighs either outside or between his. It is interesting to note that the oldest illustration of coitus yet discovered, one from the Paleolithic Solutrian age, found in Dordogne, France, depicts the man lying flat while the woman squats over him.

This is similar to the astride position, in which the woman sits upon or kneels across the man's body, while he draws up his legs to support her back. The clitoris has excellent contact with the penis in this position, but care must be exercised that it does not penetrate too deeply.

The side-by-side position was highly recommended by the poet, Ovid, in his famous work, "The Art of Love", as affording not only the greatest comfort, but the ability to prolong intercourse for a long period. In this position, the couple lie on their sides facing each other. The woman places her upper thigh over the upper thigh of the man so he can enter freely. It has the advantage that the couple can pass into sleep following coitus without separating. It is also recommended during pregnancy, as reducing strain and danger of injury.

The rear-entry position is also practiced for a variety of reasons. In this variation, the man lies on his side in back of the woman, both facing the same way. He must lie lower in the bed than she, to get under the swell of the buttocks, but it can be quite satisfactory for him. The woman, however, may find it less pleasing because the penis has no contact at all with the clitoris. While the man can easily reach it and massage it with his fingers during coitus to bring about simultaneous orgasm, it has not the same effect as when stimulated by the penis. This position is recommended only during pregnancy and illness.

The kneeling position is also a rear-entry position. The woman kneels and the man kneels behind and over her. After entrance, he will have to reach her clitoris for manual stimulation, because, as above, the penis will not be in contact with it. The knee-chest position, a variation of the kneeling position, is recommended for women who find it difficult to become pregnant because of a "tipped womb". She kneels on the bed in a deep bend, her chest resting on the bed as close to her knees as possible. This throws the uterus forward into proper position and lines up the cervix with the vaginal orifice. The woman is advised to remain in this position for some time (at least one-half hour) after intercourse so that the semen can bathe the cervix and aid the passage of sperm into the uterus.

Then there is the sitting position, in which the man sits on a chair without arms and the woman sits on his lap. The chair should be low enough for her to be able to keep her feet on the floor comfortably. This will permit her great activity in coitus, and good contact between penis and clitoris.

These are basic positions. There are others, such as standing. There are variations which will occur to a lively imagination. Try them. Never hesitate to experiment. Bear in mind several important things—full satisfaction and simultaneous orgasm come with practice; the penis should always be in contact with the clitoris if possible; and especially, remember that anything that pleases a couple is perfectly proper to do. When your door is shut behind you, you are in your own world. Whatever occurs between you, if you both derive pleasure from it, is right and good and normal.

First intercourse

The "first night" has long been a subject of public jest, and only too often of private tragedy. The sex education of most girls is compounded of ignorance, gossip, erroneous information and nervous apprehension. They expect almost anything, from pain and torture to incredible ecstasy from their first coitus. Far too many men, due to their own ignorance or selfishness, come closer to producing the first result than the second.

Most men come to marriage with some degree of sexual experience. Even where such experience has been slight, they do not have the apprehension of the unknown. The bride looks to her husband for assurance and confidence. It is of far greater importance for their future happiness that he prove his love and thoughtfulness than that the marriage be immediately and forcefully consummated. Legalized rape is no more excusable than rape outside the limits of the law.

The loving and considerate bridegroom will "make haste slowly", wooing and petting his bride and rousing her own natural desires. Patience, tenderness and ample preliminary love-play should bring a woman to the utmost degree of passion and assure her full cooperation. The first intercourse can be successful, and even completely painless, if the woman is fully ready and the man forbears to force his way. It is wise to make generous use of a good lubricant (surgical lubricating jelly is the best), whether or not a condom is used.

Many women, before marriage, practice stretching the hymen with their fingers. This is a useful procedure to assure that the hymen will not interfere with entrance or interrupt pleasure with pain. Some women, however, have very thick hymens which must be treated surgically before intercourse is possible. This is a simple matter, done in a physician's office under local anesthesia.

CHAPTER FOUR

SEX DESIRE AND FRIGIDITY

A great many people have long held the mistaken belief that women experience neither sex desire nor sex pleasure. This notion reached its height during the Victorian era, and in spite of great medical and social advances in sex knowledge, still lingers. We pay for our ignorance of the true facts with unhappy marriages and broken homes.

Throughout the centuries, scientists have studied the problem of whether man or woman had greater desire or greater capacity. Hippocrates, the father of medicine, was credited with the statement that men enjoy coitus more but women's enjoyment lasts longer. Other observations were added through the years but no one ever claimed that women had no sex feelings whatsoever. It remained for Victorian physicians to sweepingly assert that "nice" women never had sex desire and that no woman was capable of real sex pleasure and satisfaction.

This strange theory, completely contrary to the laws of nature, still persists to some extent. It is part of a whole false pattern of life that must be destroyed if people are ever to achieve real happiness in marriage. The way to destroy it is by sound sex education.

Modern scientists are agreed that the sex impulse in men and women is about equal. The biological fact that men play a more active role sexually than women does not mean that their needs or capacities are any greater. Sex desire, like sex capacity, varies among individuals but not between the sexes as a whole. One of the chief proofs of woman's sexual capacity is her ability to experience more orgasms than her husband during each act of intercourse.

The sex impulse in women, especially those with little or no sex experience, lies dormant. It is only when the woman is fully awakened to the joys of love that the conscious desire for the sex act is aroused in her. Some authorities maintain that woman does not reach the topmost peak of sexual desire until she is in her late twenties. But nearly all women have a sex impulse and absence or suppression of desire is extremely harmful and affects the very roots of marriage.

Frigidity is that state where there is no apparent sex impulse. The frigid woman feels no desire, finds no pleasure in intercourse, may even experience great disgust and hatred for the act. There are two types of frigidity, physical and psychological. There is also a condition known as complete sexual anesthesia, which is very rare, in which there is no sex feeling whatsoever. Physical frigidity is due to hormonal deficiencies, glandular disturbances or other physical reasons. It can usually be materially helped by medical treatment.

Psychological frigidity is what is usually meant when the term "frigid woman" is used. There are unusually high estimates of the number of women who are frigid. The figures are undoubtedly highly overrated. Frigidity is not a fixed state but varies from woman to woman and in the same woman at different times.

THE SEAT OF
PSYCHOLOGICAL FRIGIDITY

Psychological frigidity is caused by a false conception of what is correct and incorrect in marital relations. The first seeds of frigidity are planted by the misguided mother who checks the small child's curiosity about the genitals

55

with admonitions that it is naughty to touch, frequently accompanied by a slap on the hands. This is followed at later periods with evasions, vague rambling lectures, embarrassment and miseducation. Far too many girls grow up without a sound basic understanding of the role and functions of woman.

The instillation of fear, plus a lack of knowledge of sex and of contraception work together to warp the mind of the frigid woman. Add to this, a lack of understanding on the part of the husband, due to faulty sex education or selfishness, and an unsuccessful marriage will definitely result.

The behavior of the husband and his attitude toward his wife will have a great bearing on her possible frigidity. Sexually, the woman is dependent on the man. He plays, as we pointed out, a more active role in sex, the woman a more passive one. An inexperienced husband, or one who is selfish in his sex relations, can do serious harm to his wife's whole sex life. The practice of withdrawal as a contraceptive measure may have a bad effect because the failure to achieve orgasm leaves the woman with congested sex organs and in a state of nervous tension and dissatisfaction.

Impotence in the husband, of which premature ejaculation is the most common factor, can also induce frigidity by constant disappointment and frustration. As with frigidity, there are both physical and psychological causes for impotence. Premature ejaculation is psychological in origin. Most of the following discussion of frigidity applies as well to premature ejaculation.

Most frigidity can be overcome. A couple must understand that marriage is a give and take proposition. The first embraces are merely the first steps toward unity. It takes a long time and willing effort to create a real marriage. Both husband and wife require a thorough education in sex anatomy and function. They should learn the correct techniques of the sex act.

The husband must patiently study his wife, learn how to stimulate her desire and find the key to providing the best means of pleasing her (see Chapter 3—"Intercourse"). His tact and wisdom in overcoming the effects of premarital apprehensions, false standards and unpleasant experiences can go a long way toward achieving success. He will also find that his own pleasure will increase and will last longer as his wife responds to his considerate behavior. It is the paradox of love that each partner finds his own happiness and satisfaction increasing with every effort to bring greater joy to the other partner.

The wife, on her part, can make her sex life more happy by facing her problem honestly. She must understand that disinterest or disgust in sexual matters is no indication of special virtue or great spirituality and refinement. It is a defect of her essential womanhood, a lack of physical and emotional qualities. Instead of evading the problem by pretended headaches, tiredness, feigned illness or any of the many excuses the reluctant wife offers, she should discuss the problem frankly with her husband and try, together with him, to improve conditions. She should certainly visit her physician. If he is unable to help her, he will recommend a competent psychiatrist.

FERTILIZATION

1st DAY

2nd DAY

3rd DAY

4th DAY

5th DAY

THE FIRST FIVE DAYS
IN THE DEVELOPMENT
OF THE FERTILIZED
OVUM

CHAPTER FIVE

PREGNANCY

"Be fruitful and multiply and replenish the earth"
GENESIS *Chapter 1 Verse 28*

Fertilization takes place in the fallopian tube, where the upward moving sperm meets the downward moving egg. Although millions of sperm are ejaculated at one time and thousands may reach the tube, only one sperm penetrates the egg. The blending of the chromosomes of the sperm and egg start the new life. Chromosomes are present in all the cells of the body. They occur in pairs, two of each kind in every cell. But conception makes one cell, the fertilized egg, out of two, sperm and egg. When they unite, the number of chromosomes must be reduced, otherwise the new individual would have double the number of chromosomes typical for his species. Nature, therefore, discards half the number of chromosomes of each sex cell, so that when joined, the new cell would have the proper number.

Sex is determined by what are called the "X" and "Y" chromosomes. There are twenty-three pair of mated chromosomes in every cell, and in addition, in the male, there is an unmatched pair, one "X" and one "Y". The female has only "X" chromosomes. When the sex cells discard half their chromosomes, the female is left with one "X", but the male has either an "X" or "Y". If the "X" chromosome remains, then a female child must result, because it will have two "X" chromosomes. If a "Y" remains, the child will be a boy. As yet the individual has no control over the process.

58

Fertilization of the Ovum and Implantation of Fertilized Ovum into the Lining of the Womb

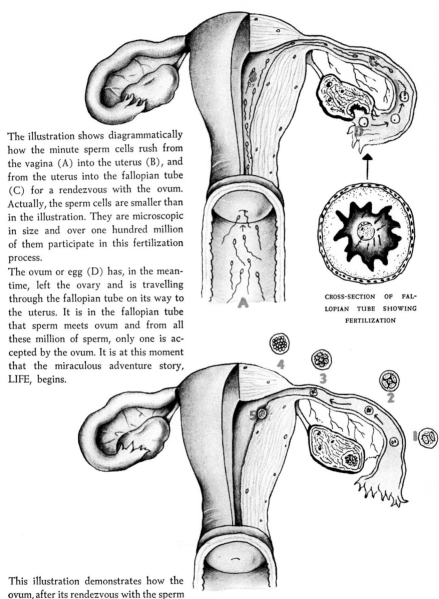

The illustration shows diagrammatically how the minute sperm cells rush from the vagina (A) into the uterus (B), and from the uterus into the fallopian tube (C) for a rendezvous with the ovum. Actually, the sperm cells are smaller than in the illustration. They are microscopic in size and over one hundred million of them participate in this fertilization process.

The ovum or egg (D) has, in the meantime, left the ovary and is travelling through the fallopian tube on its way to the uterus. It is in the fallopian tube that sperm meets ovum and from all these million of sperm, only one is accepted by the ovum. It is at this moment that the miraculous adventure story, LIFE, begins.

CROSS-SECTION OF FAL-
LOPIAN TUBE SHOWING
FERTILIZATION

This illustration demonstrates how the ovum, after its rendezvous with the sperm continues on its way along the fallopian tube to the uterus, where it immediately implants itself in the endometrium of the uterus. From the moment of fertilization, the miraculous process of growing begins and by the time the ovum implants itself, it is already well on its way to the final development.

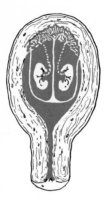

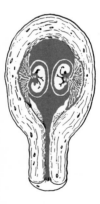

The chromosomes contain the genes, which are the carriers of all the inherited characteristics of all the ancestors of the individual. They are the reason cows always have calves and people produce babies. As *Genesis* records: "And the earth brought forth grass, and herb *yielding seed after his kind*, and the tree *yielding fruit, whose seed was in itself, after his kind:* And God saw that it was good". Each species has its own chromosome pattern and genes bearing its heritage. The blending of the many different strains within the species gives rise to new combinations and constant variations. Junior may have Mother's eyes, but he has his paternal grandmother's nose and second-cousin Tilly's red hair. Not only physical but mental characteristics, as well as traits of character are inherited through the genes from one generation to the next. Tantrums and stubbornness always come from the "other side of the family".

When the impregnated egg reaches the uterus after its journey from the fallopian tube, it attaches itself to the endometrium (lining of the uterus) and becomes embedded there. Menstruation ceases because the materials that would have been sloughed off (shed) as useless if the egg had not been fertilized, are now needed to nourish the foetus.

A healthy woman, who has always been regular in her menstrual cycle, can assume she is pregnant if her period is several days late. Other changes occur slowly, and unless one of the tests for pregnancy is employed, her physician cannot be absolutely certain that she is pregnant until several weeks have gone by.

Pregnancy tests

Since his earliest history, man has sought ways to de-

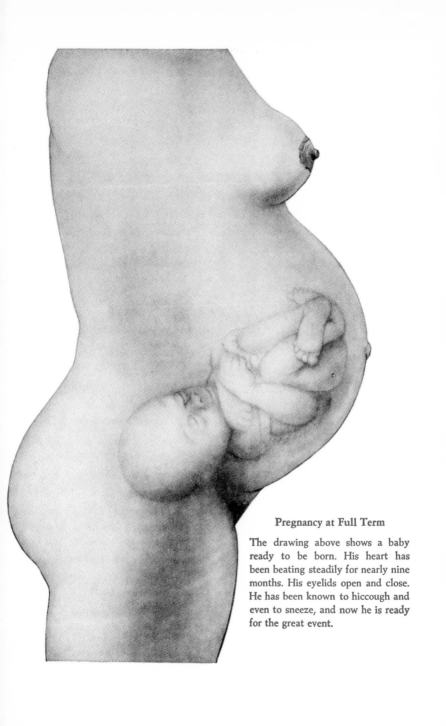

Pregnancy at Full Term

The drawing above shows a baby ready to be born. His heart has been beating steadily for nearly nine months. His eyelids open and close. He has been known to hiccough and even to sneeze, and now he is ready for the great event.

termine pregnancy. The ancient Egyptians believed that the urine of pregnant women contained material that promoted growth. To test for pregnancy, they would pour the patient's urine on young plants. If they sprouted before similar but untreated plants, it was considered a positive diagnosis. It took four thousand years to prove they were on the right track.

During pregnancy, large quantities of gonadotropic hormones are present in the urine. This urine forms the basis for nearly all the proved pregnancy tests. In 1928, the scientists Aschheim and Zondek discovered these hormones and devised their now-famous A-Z test. Since then, several other scientists have made improvements in the test and cut down the time it takes to get results. Aschheim and Zondek used immature mice. Friedman developed the test for rabbits, while Kupperman and Greenblatt used young rats and devised a different technique. Essentially, however, the test is the same.

Some of the urine of a woman believed pregnant is injected into the laboratory animal (only female animals are used, of course). After varying periods of time, depending on the animal used and the technique followed, the ovaries of the animal are examined. If the woman is pregnant, the ovaries show marked changes.

The "frog" test, which has been used in Europe for years and is becoming popular here as the "frogs" become available, is the simplest and cheapest of the tests. The creatures are not actually frogs, but a different amphibian resembling frogs, imported from South Africa. For this test, the urine requires some preparation, then is injected into the creature. Within eighteen hours, it will lay quantities of eggs if the woman is pregnant. Not only is it a highly accurate test, but it has the advantage of

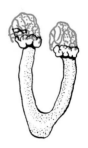

1. CONTROL ANIMAL

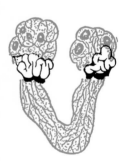

2. POSITIVE TEST
(PREGNANCY)

The Aschheim-Zondek
(A-Z) Pregnancy Test

The Baby is Ready to be Born

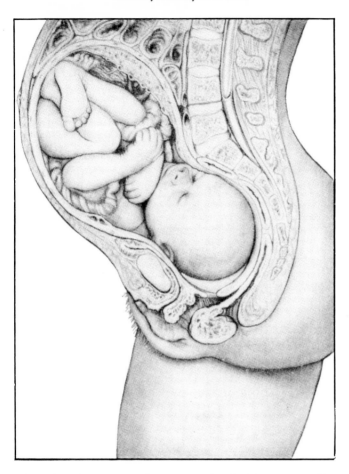

This is the highest moment of a woman's life. All of her instincts, all of the forces of nature move toward the fundamental process of reproduction, the creation of a new life. The modern woman faces this moment with greater serenity and confidence than her mother before her because she knows that science has made tremendous contributions for her safety and the welfare of her child. In the last ten years alone, infant mortality has been cut more than 50 percent. In that same time, many new discoveries have been utilized to eliminate much of the pain and most of the hazard of childbirth.

being much cheaper than the others because the "frogs" can be used indefinitely.

In the past few years, a great deal of experimental work has been done on the relationship between ovarian function and body temperature. Some scientists maintain that regardless of the length of the menstrual cycle, the body temperature rises on the fourteenth day before men struation, remaining high for the full fourteen days and dropping abruptly on the day the menses is due to start. This time of sudden rise, and not some vague "middle of the month", is considered the period of ovulation. During the ensuing forty-eight hours, the woman is fertile. According to these investigators, if the temperature does not decline on the fourteenth day, the woman can consider herself pregnant, not merely late. If the temperature drops, even though menstruation is not present, the woman is not pregnant, but delay is due to other causes. If some women do not show any marked temperature variation, it is presumed that they do not ovulate. If the woman becomes pregnant, her temperature will remain consistently high for several months, then drop.

According to these experts, all women should keep temperature charts. Those wishing to conceive should have coitus within forty-eight hours of the rise. The chart would also provide a key to ideal contraception, by avoiding coitus during this period. Some physicians claim one hundred percent contraception by this method, and excellent results in efforts to conceive. However, while the ovum is impregnable only for forty-eight hours, the sperm can live in the vagina and uterus for some time, and may be there well before the rise in temperature signals the onset of ovulation.

The method of chart keeping is simple. The tempera-

12 DAYS   **21 DAYS**   **30 DAYS**   **37 DAYS**   **50 DAYS**

Actual size drawings of embryonic development
These drawings show the baby at various stages of its development. In the first month it is extremely small, the nose, ears and the eyes appear first. In the second month, the baby is about one inch long, the head is disproportionately large because of the rapid development of the brain.

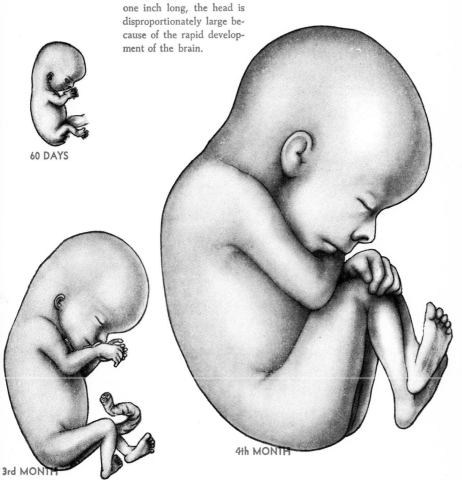

60 DAYS

3rd MONTH

4th MONTH

In the 3rd month the baby is about 3 inches long, fingers and toes are distinct with soft nails. In the 4th month it grows to about 5 inches. Sex can now definitely be differentiated and downy hair appears on the head.

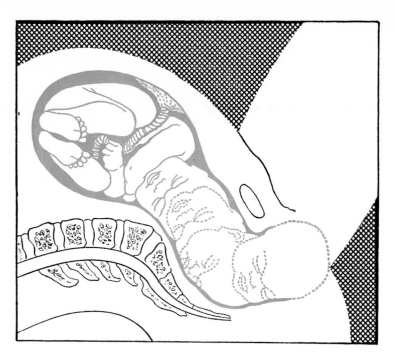

Successive steps in the birth of a baby

ture is taken (preferably rectally) every morning before getting out of bed. It is recorded on a special temperature chart, along with such pertinent items as a cold, indigestion, drinking or coitus, etc., on the previous night. Many things can cause an isolated temperature rise. After a few months of careful record-keeping, the physician is supposed to be able to determine the usual temperature rise caused by ovulation and know the period fairly accurately.

This method has been called "the poor man's Friedman test," because it costs nothing but the patient's time, an occasional check with the doctor and a thermometer, which every family should own anyway. But the chief importance of the test lies in the fact that it could, if accurate, reveal pregnancy considerably earlier than any of the other tests.

There are other tests, either not yet perfected or not sufficiently widely used to have established a body of evidence, which may prove useful eventually. One is a chemical test. Another is based on allergy test techniques. The last, when perfected, would be the fastest and easiest test, producing results in an hour.

Early diagnosis of pregnancy is extremely important in many ailments, where therapeutic abortion would have to be practiced, or in emergencies, such as suspicion of tubal pregnancy. Then, fast diagnosis is essential.

CHAPTER SIX

AS THE TWIG IS BENT

"Ye shall know the Truth, and the Truth shall
make you free."

The young couple who have come so far in seeking
knowledge are already preparing for the next step: rais-
ing their own youngsters in an atmosphere of enlighten-
ment and understanding. The modern parent, recognizing
the emotional difficulties stemming from his own bad sexual education, is anxious that his children receive intelligent information. Yet, because he learned the hard way,
he is confronted with many serious problems. How does
one discuss sex with children? How much should they
learn? At what age do I start? Must I explain about intercourse? Suppose they ask embarrassing questions, how
do I put them off without saying the wrong thing? What
will the neighbors think? Will sex knowledge prevent
juvenile delinquency? Should boys and girls be told the
same things? Do I educate the boys and my wife the
girls? Etc.

Let's start with the most serious and pressing problem,
today, that of juvenile delinquency. Sex information of
itself will not curtail delinquency. The atmosphere in
which the child acquires his learning *can* curtail it. In
other words, it is not the bare collection of facts, but the
home surroundings, attitudes of parents, the emotional
temperature of the home, which really decides whether
a child will become a useful, honored citizen or pass from
juvenile mischief to major crime. The delinquent is an

unhappy, maladjusted, emotionally insecure child. Parents who are happy together, who are sexually adjusted themselves and surround their children with love and understanding are not likely to have delinquency problems. When parents set a standard, not by lectures and punishment, but by their own outlook and behavior, the child, conditioned to it from birth, is most likely to follow the pattern.

Even before there are any children, the thoughtful young couple have begun to set the emotional atmosphere of their home by their freedom and frankness with each other; by abandoning prudery and all false modesty; by practicing the utmost thoughtfulness and consideration for each other. The eagerly awaited child is born into a world of love and intelligent care.

From the very beginning, his parents never, by tone, word, or facial expression, show disgust, annoyance or amusement at his physical functions or parts of his body. Even very young babies are quick to grasp the meanings of voice tones, which is why we always talk gently and gaily even to infants. Never pull a baby's hands away from his genitals or show disgust when he happily dabbles in his feces. To a child, everything in the world is of interest and everything is brand-new, from the fuzzy feel of his teddy bear to the slippery feel of his stool, from the taste of sugar to the taste of urine. His alert senses are amazingly quick to grasp parental attitudes.

The child begins to learn as soon as it is born. As it perceives and senses things, it stores the accumulated knowledge in its brain, often in the subconscious. It takes for granted the familiar. Having seen his parents unclothed from infancy, he will know the difference between men and women without ever thinking consciously about it.

Children develop at different rates. Usually, by the time a child is two years old, he will be able to identify by their correct names all the parts of his body, even if he cannot yet pronounce them. The growing mind is interested in everything around him. The busy little brain is always at work, figuring out this strange new world and the queer antics of adults. The questions, when they come, embrace every possible subject and all are equally important to the young seeker after knowledge. "Where does rain come from?" is as interesting to a child as "where do babies come from?" Unfortunately, most parents answer the one question briefly, casually and as correctly as possible, while the other calls forth varying emotions, which, even if suppressed, are felt instinctively by the child. The question is ignored, brushed aside, answered falsely, or, even when the truth is told, answered with too much emphasis and frequently with too much information. It is enough to say at this early stage, "from inside the mother's body."

The little child who wants to know why the stars shine, could not absorb a lecture on astronomy. The child who wants to know how babies are made cannot absorb a full-blown lecture on genes, chromosomes, and the general theory of reproduction. He should be told that when the egg-cell from the mother and the sperm cell from the father meet, a new baby is started. From there, you go on at intervals and usually in reply to questions to explain that a baby takes a long time to grow. First it is a tiny spot, then it grows bigger and bigger, in a special sac called the uterus which is inside the mother, until it is fully formed and ready to be born. It comes out of the mother through a special opening called the vagina.

The child who has been brought up in freedom of

70

thought and speech will, as he grows older, ask more searching questions. The thrilling adventure of birth and growth are laid before him in a richly glowing tapestry, the pattern revealing its intricacies as the youthful mind and emotions expand. The role of the father will be amplified; not only his immediate sexual role, but the father as guardian and protector of the home. The necessity for choosing a mate wisely, building a home for the babies to come to, the one-ness of the family unit—will be slowly and subtly built up in the child's consciousness, so that it will emerge into maturity with sound principles and high ideals.

Dr. Belle S. Mooney, whose excellent little volume, *How Shall I Tell My Child?* is a "must" for thoughtful parents, emphasizes: "Let us fully realize that sex education is more than a collection of biological facts, it is a preparation for fine living. Its ultimate purpose is to avoid mental and emotional conflict during adolescence and to develop self-confidence. The ability to meet life's demands and contacts with equilibrium and self-respect, instead of distracting wonder and fear and a dark groping for realities—all this cannot be developed from a foundation of untruths and evasions. . . . Little by little and through endless seeking to learn life's highest satisfaction and the hope of living its best—intellectually, emotionally, sexually—there should grow the conviction that sex is fine and beautiful, that it is an infinitely precious treasure to be hoarded and cherished for its ultimate splendid purpose—the most exalted goal of human relationship in mating and marriage."

From the foregoing, you have found the answers to most of the questions posed at the beginning of this chapter. One discusses sex with children exactly as one discusses everything else, no difference of emphasis. They should learn all they want to know, at the level their questions are framed. You start answering at the age they start asking the questions. You cannot talk about sex without explaining intercourse—and here I should like to emphasize a point. The young child learns first about intercourse in connection with producing babies, because his interest and hence his questions are centered there. The older child will begin to learn that intercourse is practiced for other reasons. Outside sources, friends, schoolmates, newspapers, books and movies teach him that sexual relationships are more complicated than the, to him, simple factor of producing babies. The older child should learn that sexual intercourse *between two people who love and honor each other deeply,* is the source of the greatest happiness and enriches their love still further.

Never evade or refuse to answer a question. The "embarrassment" is all on your side. Think the thing through and it will become simpler than you suppose.

One of the biggest problems in sex education is "the neighbors." It is hard to encourage freedom and unselfconsciousness at home, yet attempt to restrain children in public or with their friends. There are many parents still who confuse "ignorance" with "innocence" and believe it to be the greatest virtue instead of a serious threat to future life-adjustment. In whatever form the problem arises, the most important factor is the effect on your child. You cannot allow your neighbors' backwardness to arouse guilt feelings in your child, yet he cannot be cut off from contact with playmates of his own age. So your child's educational needs may well broaden to include missionary work among his playmates' parents. The education of the child can become, as it should, the awaken-

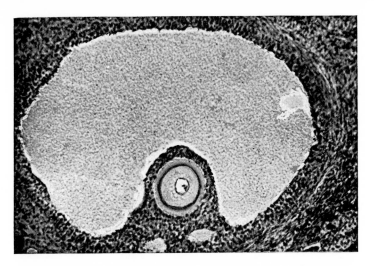

Photomicrograph of a cross-section through a human ovary showing the rarely-seen Graafian follicle and ovum.

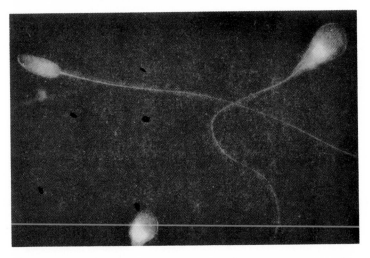

Photomicrograph of human live spermatozoa. These sperm are extremely active and difficult to photograph.

ing of your segment of the community, to go on to school through parent-teacher groups, etc.

Boys and girls should certainly learn the same things. About reproduction in general, to begin with, and then later about each other's specific development, functions and needs. Only in this way can they grow up to be thoughtful, considerate helpmeets.

To the couple who have studied this book from the beginning, the answer to the last question is clear. Both parents discuss all problems freely with all their children, preferably all together. The younger child may not follow the discussion fully, but he will grasp the essential element—that all problems are thrashed out in family conclave, and that there is nothing that is wrong to talk about in the home circle.

Life with the adolescent is frequently more complicated, but the authors do not feel that it is within the scope of this volume to expand on these problems. It is our intention here merely to point the way for the young parents. The authors are preparing a picture-story book on sex for children. In addition to our own forthcoming volume, there are many excellent books on all phases of sex education; books for the child and books for the parents. It is to be hoped, however, that our readers will not shirk their responsibility by relying on books. Those intended for the parent should by all means be studied. But it is not enough to hand a book to a questioning child. It is far better for the parent to familiarize himself with the contents of the book, then retell it to the child in his own words, or read it together with him, discussing it as they read. The authors also suggest that the illustrations in this volume can form a fascinating picture-book for youngsters, and may be used to illuminate the answers to questions, though not quite as simply as the forthcoming book. Embarrassment can be avoided in such instances as when the child wants to "see where the baby comes out". Take up the book and show him. It is easy to trace the path on a picture, because we can see inside. Similar problems will always crop up. Be prepared by having your simple facts at hand, and easy to understand illustrations available.

Appended to this chapter is a brief list of just a few of the many excellent books and pamphlets available for child guidance. Take advantage of the help that is available, some through Government agencies and others through many excellent groups such as the Child Study Association.

FOR PARENTS

How Shall I Tell My Child?, by Belle S. Mooney, M.D.
Your Child From Six to Twelve, by Children's Bureau, F.S.A., Washington, D.C.
When Children Ask About Sex, by Child Study Association.

FOR CHILDREN

The Wonder of Life, by Milton I. Levine, M.D., & Jean H. Seligmann.
Growing Up, by Karl de Schweinitz.
From Head to Foot, by Alex Novikoff.
Egg to Chick, by Millicent E. Selsam.

CHAPTER SEVEN

STERILITY

Every happily married couple want children, but a large percentage are doomed to disappointment. Nearly ten percent of all marriages are involuntarily childless. Between one-third and one-half of all sterile marriages are due to factors on the husband's side. As Dr. Abraham Stone mentions in *"A Marriage Manual"*, "Formerly it was the woman who was nearly always considered responsible for a sterile mating, and even today we are more apt to regard her as being at fault when a union proves to be childless. Barrenness has always been looked upon not only as an unfortunate circumstance, but also as a source of reproach to the woman. In many countries sterility is a cause for divorce, and the childless woman is regarded with contempt and scorn." It is important to their marital happiness that sterile couples realize that the causes may lie with the husband or be shared by both.

There are many factors involved in childlessness. The causes are not always apparent or simple to cure. However, it is not a hopeless condition. Some physicians have estimated good results in as high as 40 percent of sterility cases.

In these days of intense competition and economic tension, couples are frequently forced to wait past their first youth until they feel themselves financially able to have children. This is particularly true when the wife works. On the other hand, the wife's age plays a large part in determining her fertility, and once she has passed the peak, it may be harder for her to conceive, though not necessarily impossible.

A healthy, well-nourished female develops an egg every month from puberty to menopause. Normally, she should be able to conceive easily during these years. A healthy man manufactures millions upon millions of spermatozoa, at least one hundred million of which are ejaculated in each act of intercourse. It takes only one sperm to impregnate the egg. So the man *should* have no difficulty in fathering a child, especially as, in his case, age is of little importance. Yet the fact remains that many couples are childless against their will.

Most medical authorities agree that a couple should not consider themselves sterile until at least one year to two years of intercourse without contraception. If the couple are convinced of sterility, they should not be discouraged and resign themselves to an empty home, but should seek expert assistance. Their private physician can recommend a specialist in this field, or they can avail themselves of the facilities of the Planned Parenthood Clinics attached to many hospitals or under the auspices of the Planned Parenthood Federation of America.

It should be clearly understood that the husband should be examined first. Tests of his fertility are simple and are easily made in an office visit. Testing of the wife is a long, tedious and occasionally uncomfortable procedure, although not even the most complicated tests require anesthesia or produce pain.

The greatest mistake a couple can make is to assume that because a man is potent he must also be fertile. On the contrary, some quite impotent men have been found to be fertile and could well have impregnated females if they could have delivered the seed. Also, the fact that a

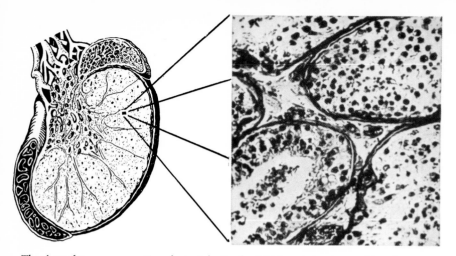

The above shows a cross-section of a testicle. On the right is a photomicrographic enlargement of the small section of testicular tissue pin-pointed on the left. The photomicrograph shows four part-sections of seminiferous tubules with extensive development of sperm. Normally, there are about one hundred million spermatozoa per cubic centimeter of semen. Although variations from the usual form occur frequently in normal semen, a certain percentage of normal forms must be present for conception to take place.

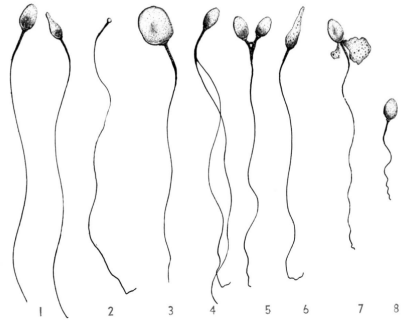

1   2   3   4   5   6   7   8

Normal and Abnormal Forms of Sperm

1—Normal sperm, front and side views; 2—pinhead; 3—giant head; 4—double tail; 5—double head; 6—elongated head; 7—undeveloped sperm; 8—short tail.

It is now believed that these malformations are possibly sperm in their immature form.

man may have fathered a child earlier in life does not mean that he is still fertile.

The husband, then, will be examined first. This is what will happen to him: A checkup on his general health, with emphasis on previous diseases, especially childhood diseases like mumps or high fever diseases like malaria. Venereal disease, past or present, is an important factor. The doctor will note his sexual development, size of genitals, distribution of body hair and fat, as a clue to the state of his endocrine development. The vas deferens will be examined for obstructions. First and most important of all, a sperm count will be made, to prove the presence of a sufficient number of active sperm in his semen.

Undescended testicles, atrophy or disease of that organ, exposure to X-ray, poisons, such as lead or alcohol, or underdeveloped or malformed penis, or premature ejaculation or impotence are possible causes of male sterility.

If the man is pronounced fertile, the wife then undergoes her series of tests. Her medical history is checked, plus a detailed record of her menstrual history since puberty. This is followed by a vaginal examination to determine the condition of the tract and the internal organs. It is now recognized that a "tipped womb", for which far too many women have been operated, does not preclude pregnancy. If the uterus is badly displaced, preventing direct insemination, there are ways to handle the problem much safer and easier than the serious method of operation. Dr. E. C. Hamblen, Associate Professor of Obstetrics and Gynecology of Duke University School of Medicine, states unequivocally that women have had far too much surgery done on their female organs, sometimes without knowing what was done or why.

It is impossible to study the egg, counterpart of the sperm, so endocrine findings must be obtained in a roundabout way. General endocrine development can be determined by the development of the breasts and genitals, distribution of hair and fat, etc. The level of ovarian function may be determined by an endometrial biopsy test. A post-coition test will show if sperm are being delivered properly to the cervix.

Blockage of the fallopian tubes is one of the most common causes of sterility in women. This can be studied by certain tests, which consists of passing either a special gas or iodized oil through the uterus, into the tubes. Chart recordings, fluoroscope or X-ray will then show if the tubes are blocked anywhere, preventing descent of the egg and its meeting with the sperm.

The Rubin test and the endometrial biopsy test, while not painful and not requiring local anesthesia, do cause considerable discomfort. Nor is it pleasant for a woman to be frequently examined vaginally. These considerations should be sufficient to impel a thoughtful husband to undergo his much simpler tests first.

Physical causes of female sterility include underdeveloped reproductive organs; obstructions of the vagina by fallen uterus, tumors, etc.; acid vaginal fluids which kill sperm; failure of the lining of the uterus, the endometrium, to properly prepare a bed for the fertilized egg.

Dr. J. Jay Rommer, author of "Sterility", emphasizes that there are psychogenic and neurogenic causes for sterility as well as physical. These factors cause a hormonal imbalance which affects fertility. Dr. Rommer has also found that allergy and associated conditions may cause sterility.

Neurogenic sterility can be caused by disorders of the

nerves supplying the pelvic region; by painful intercourse due to spasmodic contractions of the vagina; (this can also be of psychological origin); severe neuralgia in other parts of the body; chronic alcoholism or addiction to narcotics.

Psychogenic sterility can be caused by serious mental disorders such as schizophrenia, but it can also be caused by depression, worry and fear. Sometimes, the hunger for a child will cause endocrine imbalance and prevent conception. That may be why some sterile women become fertile after adopting a child and appeasing the intensity of maternal hunger. Sterility may also be caused by various fears: fear of labor-pains; subconscious fears started in childhood by a mother who maintained that coitus was painful or sinful (see "Frigidity"); fear of the husband, who may be a brute or a drunk; fear of giving bir·h to abnormal or deformed children; fears due to sexual perversions, chronic masturbation, etc. Severe shocks of various kinds can cause endocrine imbalance and therefore sterility.

Frigidity and the lack of sexual gratification may also be a factor, although many women conceive without desire or pleasure.

The allergic basis of some sterility is a newly-explored field. The large quantities of adrenalin taken by an asthmatic woman may produce hormonal imbalance and cause sterility. Also, there are some women who seem to be allergic to semen and sperm. This antipathy creates antibodies and prevents conception.

Another thing that must be remembered is that a couple may be sterile with each other, yet, on divorce and remarriage, both will raise families. This will occur when two people of low fertility are married to each

81

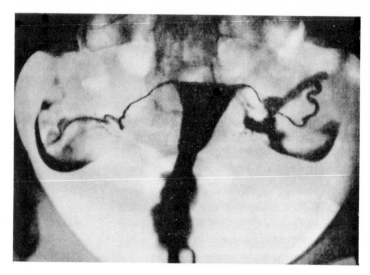

The above is a photograph of a Uterosalpingogram. It shows a normal uterus with normal open fallopian tubes.

UTEROSALPINGOGRAPHY: VISUALIZATION OF THE UTERUS AND FALLOPIAN TUBE

This Uterosalpingogram shows definite blockage of both fallopian tubes. This patient cannot become pregnant, without further medical treatment.

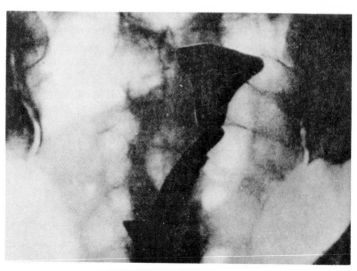

other. On remarriage to people with high fertility, conception will ensue.

The reason that sterility is not necessarily incurable is that it is made up, usually, of several factors that could be more aptly described as lessened fertility. There are, of course, some cases which are beyond medical aid, but the majority of cases, far from being hopeless, require patience, time, and of course expert medical care.

Science is making new discoveries and checking old theories every day. The question of nutrition, proper diet, is one that is being constantly studied. It has been found that certain proteins, particularly plentiful in meat, are essential for maintaining high fertility rates.

A new theory is evolving that even slight exposure to X-ray, such as X-ray examination, can cause temporary sterility. This theory has not yet been thoroughly tested, but is under examination with many other theories, treatments, etc., all aiming to solve the heart-breaking problem of involuntary sterility. Until science has found the means of providing children for every couple who desire them, adoption and artificial insemination will continue to be the means of trying to satisfy the basic natural urge for offspring.

"Test-tube" babies enjoyed a newspaper fad for some time, although "test-tube" is an incorrect phrase. Artificial impregnation is a sound medical procedure that does not need the sensationalism of the Sunday papers. In fact, the first artificial insemination was performed experimentally nearly one hundred and fifty years ago. If a woman is fertile, she can be impregnated artificially in the doctor's office. This procedure is basically simple. The physician chooses the most fertile period, around ovulation time. As few women know exactly when they ovulate, several

83

treatments are usually necessary, covering the period during which ovulation is presumed to take place. The physician injects the semen directly into the cervix, assuring conception if the egg is ready. This procedure is most frequently used when the husband has low fertility, with not enough sperm present, or not enough motility in the sperm, or when he is impotent and cannot deliver the sperm, or when there is some impediment or malformation in either husband or wife. The semen, in these cases, is the husband's.

There is another type of artificial insemination, using a donor. Couples resort to this method when the husband is completely sterile, but the couple desire a child that will be at least the wife's, and usually when they are discouraged by the years of waiting and the multitude of complications that surround adoption in many states. The physician will secure the services of a donor, whose identity is known only to himself, and who is not only in perfect health and free from hereditary taints, but also of the same general appearance, national stock, etc., as the husband. The patients and donor have no knowledge of or contact with each other. It might as well be a saline solution or medicine that the doctor is using for all the personal element that enters into the matter. Yet, because they are dealing with the creation of life, and because the procedure is still too new to have a sufficient legal and moral base established, the physician will usually insist, for his own and the wife's protection, that husband and wife sign an agreement beforehand and that the husband legally adopt the baby at birth. The utmost secrecy surrounds the whole matter. After pregnancy is established, the wife goes to another physician, who knows nothing of the origin of the child, for prenatal care and delivery.

Unfortunately, for the majority of people, the costs surrounding this type of artificial insemination are high. The donor, though invisible and anonymous, gets well paid for his services. The physician is a specialist, skilled in a delicate technique. More than one treatment is usually needed. All of these things are expensive. The couple who choose this method of creating a family must be prepared to pay for it. Some of the advantages lie in that the baby actually is borne by the wife; that its hereditary paternal background is guaranteed by the physician in charge, unlike babies bought on the Black Market or even foundlings adopted from an orphanage; that the couple start with a brand-new baby; there is no dreary waiting for year after year, on a slowly-moving list, as in the states with strict adoption laws and strangling red-tape.

CHAPTER EIGHT

THE MENOPAUSE AND MALE CLIMACTERIC

Everyone knows that women experience a "change of life", but only comparatively recently has it been recognized that men also undergo a change.

The climacteric is the period in later life when the reproductive process slows and finally stops, and important endocrine changes take place. In the female, it is most obviously manifested in the menopause, which usually starts between the ages of forty-five and fifty. The male climacteric, during which testicular function declines, usually occurs later in middle age.

The female climacteric

CROSS-SECTION OF OVARY DUR-
ING THE MENOPAUSE

The onset of menopause occurs usually between the ages of forty-five and fifty and takes some time to be completed. Havelock Ellis remarks that menopause now occurs about five years later than it did fifty years ago. Apparently, as life expectancy increases, we retain our youth for a longer span. There is great variation in the time of onset, due to many complicated factors. Child-bearing, sex-life, general health, all have a bearing on the subject. Sometimes the menses (menstruation) will cease much earlier, there being cases on record of women in their late twenties undergoing menopause. But such cases are very rare. Certain diseases and operations on women under forty will also produce premature menopause.

Menopause means cessation of menstruation. It indicates that the ovarian function is slowing up. But it does

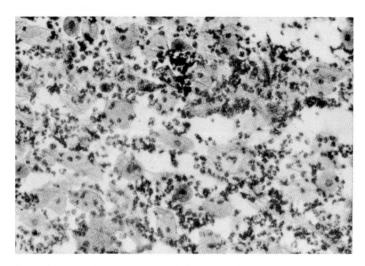

Vaginal smear taken as a means of diagnosing the menopause. Under the microscope one sees basil cells shed from the lining of the vagina.

After hormone treatment, the vaginal smear again appears normal.

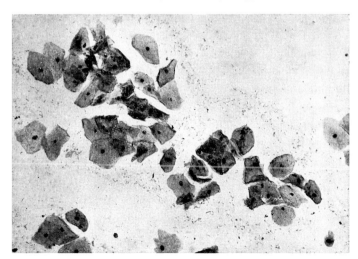

not necessarily mean that it has ceased altogether. It is not safe to abandon too early all contraceptive precautions, as many a woman who has borne a "change of life baby" can testify. It is only after menopause has been established for some time that a woman can safely assume she is sterile. It is always the wisest course to consult a good gynecologist before taking sterility for granted.

Women have always faced the prospect of menopause with dread, not only because they erroneously believed it marked the termination of their sex-life, but because of the nervous and other symptoms that accompany this period. Some of the symptoms are: extreme nervous tension, irritability, insomnia, numbness or tingling of the hands and feet, headaches of all kinds, itching of the skin, memory failure, hot flushes, a feeling of suffocation, dizziness, spots before the eyes, lassitude and constipation. Although the foregoing is a frightening list, few women have more than a couple of symptoms, and it is not necessary to suffer helplessly. Science has made the sex hormone available for treatment of these symptoms. Their administration by a competent physician will not only check the symptoms and ease the woman safely through the changeover, but will help to restore sexual desire where this has waned as part of the whole clinical picture.

It is not true that a woman's sex life is ended when her child-bearing period is past. Quite the contrary, indeed. Most women continue to have strong sexual desires and to enjoy intercourse for many years after the menopause. When all danger of conception is safely past, many women experience even greater pleasure from coitus because they feel freer to abandon themselves to it. As W. J. Fielding points out, "many women are more attractive at fifty than they were at twenty-five; and if their personality has been developed and enriched by the passing years, they may be more charming at sixty than they were at thirty."

The male climacteric

Until recently, the possibility of a male change of life was not recognized, fully, and it still is news to the average layman. The climacteric is not universal, as with women, and occurs at a later period. It is marked by nervousness, hot flushes, dizziness, headaches, etc. There is frequently a loss of sex desire and potency. Treatment with sex hormones will relieve the symptoms and restore the normal sex activity.

One thing must be borne in mind. A woman or man going through such a fundamental change needs all the loving thoughtfulness and consideration of which his partner is capable. A woman who feels neglected, no longer of interest to her husband, may sustain a psychological blow from which she will never fully recover. A man whose wife is impatient with or scornful of temporary impotence may have the greatest difficulty in overcoming it. Love and understanding and especially patience must be manifest, so that, when the temporary difficulties are adjusted, a closer unity and harmony will bind the couple.

CHAPTER NINE

APHRODISIACS

From time immemorial people have sought ways to increase their sexual desires. The "love potions" so popular in ancient times were aphrodisiacs aimed at one particular person. All sorts of drugs, herbs and substances have been used. One prescription of the middle ages lists nearly fifty ingredients, roots, flowers and herbs, and all absolutely useless. The most famous of aphrodisiacs is "Spanish Fly" which is made not from flies but beetles. It's correct name is cantharides and it is used in medicine as a counterirritant. It is not valued as an aphrodisiac despite popular stories. Modern medical sources do not record any drugs as aphrodisiacs, and most physicians discredit the value of any substance used exclusively for that purpose.

Certain drugs and treatments prescribed by physicians, such as hormones, may have an aphrodisiac effect, but they are not prescribed specifically for that, but for various ailments.

The "monkey-gland" operation popular several years ago, as well as other similiar operations, were in effect intended as aphrodisiacs, since their purpose was to restore potency. Unfortunately, the operations failed to be sufficiently useful.

Nevertheless, most people still cherish their own pet beliefs about methods to arouse sex desire. Alcohol is looked upon as a great stimulant, yet if taken in large doses, will have just the opposite effect. The man who uses the excuse "I was so drunk, I didn't know what I was doing", either wasn't that drunk or was incapable of doing it. Ether, like alcohol, first stimulates, then depresses.

Among the superstitions held over from ancient times is belief in the power of onions, garlic, raw eggs and similar things. Shellfish, especially oysters and clams, are very widely believed in. A young man of the writer's acquaintance happened to order raw clams in a restaurant. The young lady with him became frightened at what might happen as the result of a shellfish diet. She became very nervous, ate hardly anything and insisted upon being taken home immediately upon the conclusion of the meal! This modern, college-bred girl would have been scornful if offered a charm against the Evil Eye, but where sex is concerned, anything is believed.

If potency is not satisfactory, a physician should be consulted. He is best fitted to determine what is wrong and what are the best methods of treatment.

CHAPTER TEN

CONTRACEPTION

There are many reasons for contraceptive practices, starting with the horrifying realization that a healthy woman, taking no precautions, could possibly give birth to more than twenty children during her child-bearing period. Such a prospect, alone, would be enough to frighten any woman away from marriage. But every couple employs some means of birth control, even though it may be ineffective and provide only a false sense of security.

The principal reasons for birth control are child-spacing, economic (couple cannot afford adequate care for large family), conservation of maternal health, disease—either active or chronic, prevention of transmission of inheritable diseases. "In my opinion," says Dr. Stone, "birth control constitutes an important health measure. It helps to conserve the well-being of the family and the home and is an essential factor in marriage . . . the health and welfare of a family depend upon an intelligent planning of the coming of children . . . Adequate physical and mental health in marriage can indeed hardly be realized without an understanding and a knowledge of birth control."

After a long and bitter struggle, the need for birth control has been finally acknowledged. With constantly increasing data becoming available, we are close to the goal of providing help for all who seek it. However, there is, as yet, no perfect birth control method. Dr. Stone outlines

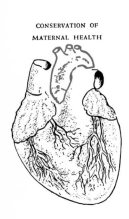

CONSERVATION OF
MATERNAL HEALTH

92

the requirements of the ideal contraceptive as follows: "It should be not only harmless and entirely reliable, but also simple, practical, universally applicable and esthetically satisfactory to both husband and wife."

Until recently, the favorite contraceptive technique advocated in birth control centers was the diaphragm and jelly method.

Diaphragm and jelly

Physicians generally are agreed that conception control should be in the hands of the woman. Since the fear of pregnancy is always with her, she is the more likely to be careful and conscientious in carrying out the precautions. The diaphragm is one of the chief methods of woman-control.

It is essential that the woman be familiar with her own anatomy, to know by touch her cervix and the space behind it. This is to assure that the diaphragm is correctly placed each time it is used.

The diaphragm must be fitted individually by a private physician or at a clinic. There is a wide variation in size, and to be effective, it must fit snugly in place but without pressure or irritation. The diaphragm is used with a contraceptive jelly or cream which aids in insertion as well as acting as a further, chemical, barrier to sperm. It must tuck up snugly behind the symphysis (pubic bone), so that the finger cannot dislodge it or push it down. If the finger can dislodge it, the thrusting penis surely will.

Some of the advantages of the diaphragm method, in addition to its very high percentage of safety (about 95%), are: it may be inserted earlier, before actual love-making begins, and thus will not interfere esthetically; it must be left in place for at least eight hours, so there is

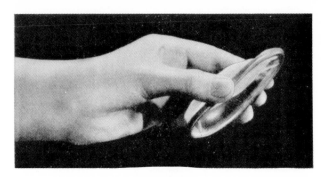

The Diaphragm

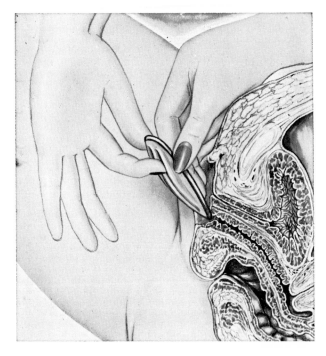

The above drawing shows how the diaphragm is inserted into the vaginal vault. (Remember, you will have to be carefully fitted for a diaphragm, and your doctor will give you detailed instructions for the correct use of the diaphragm.)

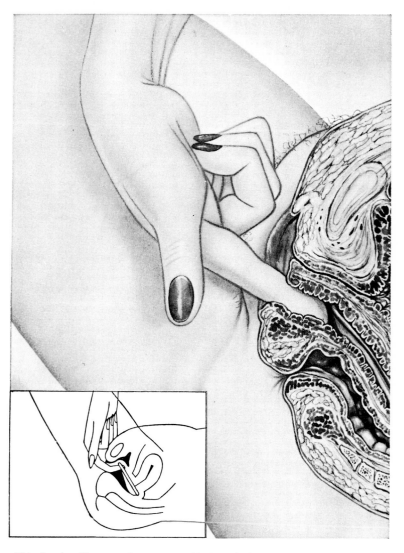

This drawing illustrates the proper positioning of the diaphragm with the index forefinger. (In the insertion) The first check point with the index finger to make sure that the diaphragm fits snugly.

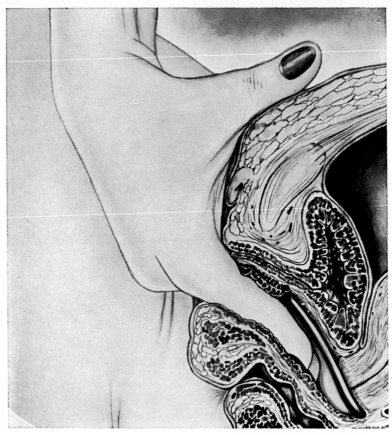

The above drawing is a test for correct diaphragm placement. It shows the index and middle finger inserted to make sure that the diaphragm has covered the cervix.

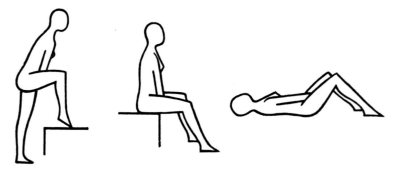

These are several suggested positions for inserting the vaginal diaphragm. Remember you can only use your diaphragm if it is properly fitted by your doctor and his instructions must be carefully obeyed.

Illustrations pages 94 through 96, courtesy of Lanteen Products, Esta Medical Laboratories no need for disturbance of rest following coitus; it does not require a douche on removal. If intercourse is repeated, it is best to insert some jelly before each session, leaving the diaphragm in place.

Cervical caps

These are, as their name implies, small rubber or plastic caps that fit directly over the cervix and are held on by suction. They are harder to apply, especially if the woman has short fingers or is fat. Since the cervix is barely an inch across and less than an inch long, the difficulties of its use can be readily understood. However, some women prefer them to diaphragms, and some have cervices which are particularly suited to this type of contraceptive device. The cervical cap must be fitted by a physician, who also examines the patient from time to time to see if it is causing irritation.

The condom

With the possible exception of withdrawal, the condom is the best-known and most widely used contraceptive. Properly used, it is one of the safest. It is the most available contraceptive, requiring no special fitting or training in its use, and can be readily purchased. Those which are sold rolled and packaged are usually of better quality and therefore more dependable than the loose, unrolled variety. In any case, each condom should be tested before using.

If it is rolled, unroll it. Blow it up like a balloon, at least to the size of a melon. Hold the open end tightly closed and listen for air-leaks. Rotate it slowly near the face, so that the tiniest wisp of air can be felt, or hold it before a strong light and look for weak spots. If none is present, roll the condom by slipping two fingers of one hand into it and rolling it carefully with the other until it is almost completely flat. It is then ready for use.

Many men object to using condoms because they claim it interferes with sensation. This may be because they were not used correctly. The condom should not be used dry but in connection with surgical lubricating jelly or vaginal (spermicidal) jelly.

When ready to use the condom, unroll it just a little, to form a small cup. Put about a teaspoonful of lubricating jelly into the cup (which should be opposite the rolled edge), and roll on to the penis. The lubricant must be inside the condom. When the condom is on, slide it back and forth to distribute the lubricant. Then apply a little jelly to the outside of the condom to make insertion easier. The use of vaginal jelly instead of lubricating jelly is to "make assurance doubly sure", and to serve in emergency if the condom should break during use or the penis shrink too rapidly after orgasm and slip out. If this occurs, there is no great cause for alarm. The sperm is inside the condom and the lower, open end outside the vagina. Just pull out the condom carefully, gathering up the edges.

After use, the condom can be tested again, this time by filling with water. If there are no leaks, wash it with warm water and soap, turn inside out and repeat. Dry thoroughly on both sides. Put it aside for a few hours, then dust thoroughly with talcum powder on both sides and roll up ready for use. A good quality condom, properly taken care of, will last for months.

Modern condoms are so thin and flexible that there is hardly any loss of sensation if they are used. Many men, however, prefer to put them on only toward the end of intercourse. This can be dangerous, because, in spite of good control, a small amount of semen may be emitted

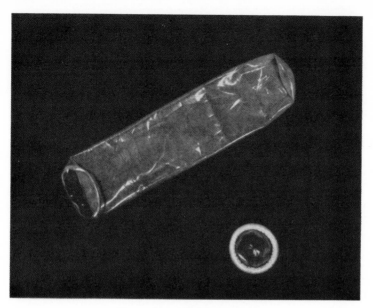

The condom rolled and unfolded

Method of testing condom (see text on page 98)

(see "withdrawal"). Also, the condom is the one invaluable protection against possible venereal infection.

Dr. Robert Latou Dickinson states that men with premature èjaculation find that the condom increases control and enables them to prolong coitus. It is also advisable where the wife is careless or has inhibitions regarding her own use of contraceptives. For the newly-married and those women who cannot be fitted with diaphragms, the condom is the ideal contraceptive.

Dr. Kelly says, "properly tested and rightly used, the condom is one hundred percent effective." Dr. Dickinson says practically the same thing, adding, "the condom is *suited* (italics his) to males with good erection."

The above method deals with the rubber condom, which is soft, flexible, with a rubber constricting ring at the base, and very much cheaper than the skin condom. The skin condom is made from the peritoneal covering of the bowels of sheep and similar animals. It is stronger and somewhat stiff, resembling fine parchment. The most expensive is softer and more flexible, but does not compare with the flexibility of rubber, because it has no elasticity and cannot be rolled up. Except for rolling, it should be handled like the rubber condoms.

One serious complaint against the condom is that the need to place it seriously impairs the emotional tension and is esthetically distasteful. If the placing of the condom is incorporated into the love-play, this need not occur.

Cream or jelly alone

Vaginal cream or jelly serves a double purpose. The jelly itself acts as a barrier closing off the opening of the cervix, and the chemicals in the jelly kill the sperm. In some surveys, it has been found to be as effective a method as the jelly and diaphragm technique. It is more likely to be wholly adequate for the woman who has never had a child, because childbirth stretches the opening of the cervix, making complete protection by this method doubtful.

Vaginal creams and jellies come with special applicators for insertion into the vagina. These are of different types but all are easy to use. They do not require any special training beyond the printed instructions that usually come with the package. The average dose, usually measured mechanically by the applicator, is about one teaspoonful, inserted high up, near the cervix, but not in the pocket behind it.

The suppository

Much has been written about the suppository. There is considerable difference of opinion as to its effectiveness.

At best, the suppository is about as effective as a jelly or cream without the use of a mechanical barrier, the diaphragm. Other considerations, such as enlarged opening of the cervix, incorrect placing of the suppository and inability of the melted suppository to reach all crevices of the vaginal vault where sperm may hide, do not make the suppository an effective contraceptive.

The authors fully agree with the report on contraceptives in *New and Non-Official Remedies* issued under the direction of The Council on Pharmacy and Chemistry, American Medical Association: "To insure further protection, physicians should advise the concurrent use of an occlusive device such as a diaphragm, and should stress the fact that suppositories or capsules used alone are less effective."

After considerable investigation the authors are convinced that the combination use of diaphragm and jelly or cream is the most effective method of contraception available today.

The rhythm method

A woman is fertile only for a very brief period following ovulation. *If one could be certain* just exactly when ovulation takes place, "natural" birth control would be very simple. Unfortunately, the whole question is actually extremely complicated.

A woman ovulates around the middle of the menstrual cycle, that is, somewhere around the fourteenth day, *if* she has a twenty-eight day period. The ovum is impregnable for a very short time, estimated by scientists as between two and twelve hours. Sperm, too, last only about forty-eight hours. So that, if a woman knew with certainty when she ovulated, control of conception would present no problem.

However, the menstrual cycle varies, even in "regular" women. The latest study (1968) on the length and variability of the human menstrual cycle which was carried out by the Center for Population Research indicates that age is a predominating factor in cycle regularity. Using 30,655 recorded menstrual cycles from 2,316 women it was found that 95% of all cycles were between 15 and 45 days long. The average number of cycles was 29.1 days with deviations of 7.46 days possible. Variability of menstrual cycle lengths were highest for women under 25 years of age and declined steadily to reach a minimum for ages 35 to 39. This study shows that the human menstrual cycle does not occur at regular predetermined intervals of 28 days and that there is a relatively large degree of variation within women.

102

Women who depend on the rhythm method must allow at least eight days for the possible fertile period. The consensus of medical opinion is that the week preceding menstruation and a very few days afterward are possibly the only safe periods.

It must be remembered further that any factor, from a cold to unusual fatigue, emotional stress, even frequent intercourse, can have a bearing on upsetting the cycle and cause early or late ovulation. It does seem obvious that prediction of ovulation date and the "safe period" by the rhythm method based upon a 28 day period is a risky undertaking.

The douche

As an accessory to feminine hygiene, the douche may be useful. As a contraceptive, despite its popularity, it is useless. Sperm travel a great deal faster than even the most nervous of women, who must leap from bed (when she should be lying relaxed and contented), and, frequently, prepare the douche before she can use it. Also, the sperm can travel where she cannot, into the cervical cavity and hence up the uterus. Dr. Dickinson comments that the important place of the douche is as an immediate auxiliary for other methods or as an emergency measure.

The douche may be prepared quite simply of warm water to which may be added such things as strong soap suds, small amounts of vinegar, lemon juice or alum. Never use lysol, bichloride of mercury or any such product without express instructions from a physician. Never use ice-cold or very hot water.

In douching, the fluid should never be forced into the vagina. Hang the bag no more than three feet above the level of the vagina. In using a bulb syringe, squeeze lightly and carefully. What is important is to tighten the vulva around the nozzle so that the vagina will become distended with water and the numerous creases and ridges smoothed out and cleaned. Fill the vagina, release the water and fill again several times to ensure successful and thorough cleansing.

Sponges and tampons

These devices are not popular in cities where other forms of contraception are available. They are useful, however, in the rural areas, out of reach of stores and medical facilities. They have the advantage of being homemade, usually of accessible material and of being cheap.

The sponge, shaped at home from a soft rubber sponge or a sea sponge, either of which can be readily bought in stores, by mail, etc., should be rounded, with a hollowed out space. Usually, a strong thread is securely sewn to it to facilitate removal, although many women do not find it necessary. There are several foam pastes and powders on the market which are used in conjunction with the sponge, although weak vinegar or thick soap lather is also used. The soap may cause irritation or slight burning in both wife and husband. The sponge is soaked in water, then squeezed almost dry. The foaming agent is applied to both sides and worked in gently to start the foam. The whole thing is inserted as far up as possible, being careful not to squeeze too hard and lose some of the foam.

The sponge can be left in until morning, but if a second intercourse follows, it is advisable to insert a second sponge over the first. On removal, the sponge should be washed with warm soapy water. Some authorities recommend douching on removal. Half the water should be used before the sponge is removed and half afterward, distending the vagina, as described above.

Tampons are wads of cotton or wool, or pieces of clean cotton cloth, usually with strings attached for removal, soaked in some home-made contraceptive such as a weak solution of vinegar or lemon juice and inserted against the cervix. Such household remedies as lemon juice or vinegar are not the surest protection.

Foams

More recent products which utilize this method of contraception (EMKO VAGINAL FOAM (Emko), DELFEN VAGINAL FOAM (Ortho)) are inserted as a pre-formed foam by means of a vaginal applicator. Widespread clinical studies of this type of product indicate that it has a fairly high degree of effectiveness.

The intracervical stem pessary

This device scarcely deserves mention in any modern book. It consists of a stem which is inserted into the cervical canal, and a cap that covers the end of the cervix. It is made in one piece, of a variety of similar forms, and used to be made of gold. It must be fitted by a physician, removed and replaced for each menstrual period, is a ladder for infection to travel straight into the uterus and its constant irritation can cause serious injury, including cancer. It is not, today, in good repute.

Withdrawal

This most ancient of contraceptive methods may be hallowed by age but not by usefulness. It is not as reliable as other methods and it may give rise to psychological disturbances, although expert medical opinion is still divided on that score. In any case, whether psychological upsets follow or not, the essential point is that it cannot be completely relied on as a contraceptive measure.

Withdrawal (coitus interruptus), as its name implies, consists of withdrawing the penis from the vagina before the act of intercourse has reached its climax for the man. Ejaculation takes place outside. For the man with good control, it may be satisfactory, but unless a woman can achieve orgasm before withdrawal it will not be satisfactory for her, even though the husband may induce orgasm by massaging the clitoris.

Quite aside from the possibility of loss of satisfaction, the main trouble with withdrawal is that it may not work. If a man has a quick emission, or if he is not sure exactly when ejaculation starts, or if the method imposes a conscious strain on him, it obviously will not be satisfactory. Many men, too, have some sperm in the mucus exuded by the tip of the glans. Then, too, if a second intercourse follows the first, there will be active sperm in the urethra, some of which is bound to escape unless the man takes the precaution of urinating first.

In addition, it is not satisfactory for the wife who cannot fully rely on her husband's control, or who cannot reach an orgasm unless the penis is in place, or who enjoys the sensation of the gush of semen in the vagina.

Other detracting factors are the need, frequently, to limit coital action for fear of losing control, the need to be constantly on guard; the lessened pleasure in the finish when mutual enjoyment should be at its height.

There is another version of withdrawal, called *Coitus reservatus,* which consists of prolonged intercourse without the man's ever reaching a climax. The woman may or may not have orgasms. This method was one practiced by a religious settlement, the Oneida Community, but has never achieved any popularity outside the group, nor is it recommended by physicians.

Physiologic conception control

Physiologic conception control is the latest and probably the most desirable and effective contraceptive method yet devised. Although the idea of controlling conception via hormonal pills has now been tested for more than fourteen years, the actual marketing of the oral contraceptive in the United States dates back only to 1961. All of the hormonal tablets available for contraceptive purposes consist of synthetic hormones which closely imitate the actions of some of the endocrine glands. When taken as directed they will prevent the ovaries from releasing ova or egg cells.

Until now contraception was limited to mechanical or physical methods: diaphragm or condoms to stop the sperms from entering the uterus, and contraceptive jelly, cream or suppository to destroy the sperms before they have a chance to penetrate the cervix on their way to the uterus.

"The pill" (all of the oral contraceptive tablets now available) consists of mixtures of two female hormones, estrogen and progestagen. In each monthly cycle the natural estrogen hormone (estradiol) is produced in increasing quantity from Day 1 (onset of menstruation) to about Day 12 to 14. Because of the increased rate of estrogen production the endometrium (lining of the uterus) thickens and becomes a potential source of nutrition for the fertilized ovum. Just about the time the endometrium reaches its maximum growth there is a slight decrease in estrogen production and the beginning of secretion by the ovary of

107

progesterone. This causes the thickened endometrium to become glandular and receptive to implantation by a fertilized ovum.

By use of the pill this sequence is disrupted and the so-called "estrogenic" and "progestagenic" phases are shifted so as to make conception impossible. The major means by which this is effected is by preventing the release of the egg or ovulation. (Ovulation is believed to result from feedback of the ovarian hormones to a part of the brain known as the hypothalamus which in turn stimulates the release of the pituitary hormones which trigger ovulation).

Failure to release the ovum or egg cell sometimes occurs normally. In such cases it results in a missed period. When taking the pills, however, the dosage regime is designed to bring about normal menstruation within the 26 to 32 day period. Menstruation in the "artificial" cycle results from the discontinuation of the estrogen-progestagen dosage just as it does in the untreated cycle when the ovaries stop producing the female hormones each month. Thus while the estrogenic hormone in the pills is the effective blocker of ovulation, the progestagen component imitates the normal ovarian secretion which results in good menstruation at the end of the cycle.

The use of the pills to produce "artificial" menstrual cycles which are not in synchrony with the natural cycle is the heart of the idea of physiologic conception control.

Since the original introduction of the pill many improvements have been made. The hormone dosage, for example, has been reduced very considerably and the subsequent discomforts caused by hormone administration have been minimized. One thing that has not been changed is the need to diligently take the pills in accordance with directions. Since the "artificial" cycle is intended not only to mimic but to alter the natural one, omission of pill taking on one or more days may allow the natural cycle (with ovulation) to occur. So called "pill failures" are mainly attributable to this cause.

The type of pills available at present can be divided into those which are a *combination* of estrogen and progestagen (orally active modifications of the natural female hormones) and the *sequential* (pills containing only the estrogen component for a number of days to block ovulation, and then followed by a combination of estrogen and progestagen to insure normal menstruation). Both of these dosage regimens are taken for from 20 or 21 days beginning on Day 5 following the onset of menstruation. At the end of Day 24 or 25 approximately 3 or 4 days may elapse before the next onset of menstruation, usually producing a normal 28 day cycle.

Since the day of menstruation very often varies in the "artificial" cycle just as it does in the natural cycle, a great deal of confusion in the past has been caused by waiting for menstruation and not resuming treatment as directed. In some cases menstruation is either delayed or does not occur at all during pill taking. Any delay in starting the next cycle of pill taking can be dangerous. An improvement has been the introduction of the 28 day regimen which contains 21 hormone pills and 7 inert pills so that there is no need to follow dates. At the end of the 28th pill a new 28 day regimen is started.

In the following table are listed the products presently approved by the Food and Drug Administration as oral contraceptives. They are classified as either combination pills or sequential pills. All of the pills in each of the categories are considered equivalent in effectiveness.

ORAL CONTRACEPTIVES

COMBINATION

NAME	COMPANY
PROVEST 10 mg.	Upjohn
ENOVID 5 mg.	Searle
ENOVID 2.5 mg.	Searle
NORLESTRIN 2.5 mg.	Parke Davis
NORINYL 2 mg.	Syntex
ORTHO-NOVUM 2 mg.	Ortho
OVULEN 1 mg.	Searle
NORINYL 1 mg.	Syntex
NORIDAY 1 mg.	Syntex
ORTHO-NOVUM 1 mg.	Ortho
NORLESTRIN 1 mg.	Parke Davis
NORLESTRIN-28 1 mg.	Parke Davis
OVRAL 0.5 mg.	Wyeth
NORINYL 1+80	Syntex
ORTHO-NOVUM 1+80	Ortho

SEQUENTIAL

NAME	COMPANY
C-QUENS	Lilly
ORACON	Mead Johnson
NORQUEN	Syntex
ORTHO-NOVUM SQ	Ortho

There is considered to be a difference in effectiveness between the combination and sequential types in that the latter may have a higher pregnancy danger in the event that one or more pills are omitted. Thus many women who feel more comfortable on the sequential regimen have a greater obligation to make sure that there are no pill omissions. "The pills" are in any event available only upon prescription by a Doctor. The Food and Drug Administration requires that full information must be provided by the manufacturer to the prescribing physician. This information is available also by way of a package insert which must accompany every package that is marketed by the manufacturer. However, prescriptions are often written in such a way that the prescribed tablets are removed from their original container and the package insert is not made available to the patient. It is, therefore, incumbent upon the user to fully avail herself of the information which should be provided by the prescribing physician both as regards to procedures to be followed, the relative efficacy and the side effects or possible dangers.

The pill as a physiologic method for conception control has revolutionized the possibilities for contraception.

Dr. Guttmacher, Chairman of a group of scientists in a symposium on OVULATION CONTROL, in his discussion of this method of contraception and the results obtained with one of these products, stated that it is "the best, the most effective contraception known to man. Its failure rate in patients who take it consistently is virtually zero. We can say this, I believe, about no other method of contraception, except perhaps chaining the husband out in the woodshed."

Since its first introduction into commercial use in 1961, more than 18,000,000 women throughout the world were using the pill in 1969. As a result of this mass exposure confusing data has been accumulated which implicate oral contraception with distressing and possibly dangerous side effects, or possibly toxic effects.

Side effects of artificial hormonally induced menstrual cycles should not be unexpected. Since millions of women are taking tablets of varied hormonal dosage, it should be anticipated that such dosages may differ from the natural hormonal level of the individual. Thus, weight gain due to excess water retention, breast fullness and nausea as a response to excessive estrogen dosage, headache and bleeding irregularities (breakthrough bleeding—intramonthly spotting) may occur in a small number of women due to the difference between the artificially induced hormonal levels and their own natural levels. These changes, if they occur, are easily endured by most oral contraceptive users. Those who find the side effects sufficiently unpleasant either discontinue or ask their physician to change the product that they are receiving.

Many women are relieved by being shifted from the combination pill to the sequential pill. Those women who have found that none of the dosage regimens provides comfort have "dropped out". The high rate of drop outs, 33% in each two year period, indicates that there is great room for improvement in the physiologic methods of conception control.

Toxic or dangerous effects may not be equated with "side effects". Side effects may be easily avoided by discontinuation of the pill. Toxic effects must not be tolerated either by the patient, the physician or the Governmental authorities. Wherever sufficient data has been accumulated that might implicate the pill as a causative factor in any illness, the Food and Drug Administration has required the manufacturer to issue warnings both in their advertising and package inserts. As of 1969, there has been no recommendation by any committee of experts appointed by the government that the use of the present pills should be discontinued.

The Medical Letter on Drugs and Therapeutics, an independent non-profit publication providing unbiased critical evaluation of drugs, stated in 1967:

"With millions of women using oral contraceptives, almost every known disorder must be expected to occur in some of the women. Whether the frequency of occurrence is significantly greater than among comparable women who do not use oral contraceptives is not yet known. There are risks in the use of oral contraceptives but they must be weighed against the greater risk for many women resulting from fear of pregnancy and from unwanted pregnancies and illegal abortion (the number of illegal abortions in the United States is estimated at about a million to a million and a half each year)."

There is no good reason why a woman who has discomfort on the pill or is concerned about possible dangerous effects cannot switch to other means of contraception, but it should be borne in mind that there are substantial differences in their effectiveness. These differences are usually stated in terms of the risk of pregnancy among 100 women each using a different method of contraception for one year (a total of 1200 menstrual cycles). Such possible risks (% of contraceptive failure) are defined below:

Douche	37.8
Foam	22.0
Jelly	20.0
Withdrawal	16.0
Condom	14.9
Rhythm	14.4
Diaphragm	12.0
IUD	3.9
Pill (Sequential)	1.4
Pill (Combination)	0.2

This, of course, does not mean that every woman using any one of these methods would encounter an identical risk of pregnancy. Statistics suffer from the fact that in most of the methods listed there are no impartial observers who can determine whether the method was used correctly at all times.

Apart from its greater contraceptive effectiveness, "the pill" has certain other advantages which have an obvious appeal to many women—as well as men. It is free from objections on esthetic grounds, it does not blunt sensation, and, since it does not involve use immediately prior to the intercourse, it does not interfere with the feeling of spontaneity which is a most desirable feature of this relationship.

Improved physiologic conception control methods under development

The next product to become available for general use will be the mini-pill. These consist of a 0.3 to 0.5 mg of a progestagen alone to be taken every day. These mini-pills may work by promoting formation of a thick mucous layer over the cervix, blocking the passage of sperm cells, although the actual mechanism is unknown. Their big advantage is that they contain no estrogen, thus eliminating the side effects and toxicity possibilities of present pills. However, they do result in frequent breakthrough bleeding and amenorrhea. As an improvement on the mini-pill, scientists are studying the possibility of a silicone plastic implant which can be placed under the skin and release a constant microdosage of progestagen over a period of a year or two, thus eliminating the need for daily mini-pill administration. Also, implants could be removed when pregnancy is desired.

Another approach is a long acting injection which will provide a dosage of progestagen for from three to six months. The disadvantage of this type of contraception is that it will prevent menstruation during this period and may cause psychological distress to the woman who counts on monthly menstruation to reassure her that she is not pregnant. This form of medication is of great interest in underdeveloped areas for use in nursing mothers since it does not interfere with their milk production.

Also, under development are the postcoital so-called "morning after" pills. These are hormone dosages which can prevent the pregnancy if taken soon enough after intercourse. Such procedures, however, cannot be constantly used since continuous and unregulated hormone dosage would cause chaotic menstrual cycles. The "morning after" pill will probably be reserved for emergency use only.

Conception control for men

Numerous studies have been carried out on the oral use of hormonal and non-hormonal compounds to prevent the production and maturation of sperm cells. Although promising results have been reported, there are a number of serious objections which have been raised against this contraceptive method.

In addition to problems of effectiveness and safety, the loss of sexual desire has been reported by some men who have tried these compounds. Also there is the important objection to this method of contraception that most women prefer to be in control of the method used. Until such time as there is definite evidence that this method of contraception is extremely effective, safe, and acceptable to both men and women, there is little likelihood that it will be used to any extent.

Intrauterine device (IUD)

This contraceptive method has been used for some years, particularly in the Far East, and originally involved the use of a flexible ring of silver wire (Grafenberg Ring) which was inserted into the uterus by a physician. The device is left in the uterus and not removed so long as contraception is desired. Increased interest in this method during recent years has resulted in the development of newer intrauterine devices made of plastic in the form of spirals, loops and bows; there is also a stainless steel ring available. The device is thought to act by creating a hostile uterine wall condition which prevents or discourages implantation of a fertilized ovum. However, the exact mode of action has not yet been determined and is the subject of considerable study.

The IUDs presently available and in wide use are the Lippes loop (Ortho) and the Saf-T-Coil (Julius Schmid, Inc.) both open devices; and the Birnberg bow (American Caduceus Industries) and the Hall-Stone ring (Glaxo-Allenburys, Ltd., England) both closed devices. Although these devices are inexpensive and quite effective, they have certain drawbacks which have not yet been overcome.

It is now clear that the IUDs must be properly inserted and fitted. Where this is done, the pregnancy rates during the first year's use vary from 1% to 3% with the Lippes loop and the Saf-T-Coil, the more reliable of the older IUDs. Thus, while the IUDs are less reliable in preventing conception than the oral contraceptives, they are more reliable than condoms or diaphragms with spermicidal agents.

A greater pregnancy risk is encountered by women who spontaneously expel the device because of poor tolerance. This expulsion may go unnoticed. Replacements with a larger device or a different shape may result in better retention. Also some women have irregular or heavy bleeding and pain. This may require removal of the device usually within the first four months of use. Patients with pain and bleeding sometimes tolerate a

116

smaller device, but the danger of expulsion is thereby increased.

Because of the concern about the side effects of oral contraceptives, many women who have stopped using the pill prefer a method such as the IUD which does not require precoital preparation.

The Medical Letter in 1969, taking into consideration the renewed interest in the IUDs, concluded that they "are effective in preventing pregnancy in most women, but they are poorly tolerated by about 30% of women, especially by young women and those who have not borne children. They are useful in women who cannot successfully use topical contraceptives before coitus and for whom the oral contraceptive agents are considered excessively hazardous or are poorly tolerated."

The "safe" period

This is the nursing period following childbirth. Many mothers do not menstruate at all during this period, some only after several months. There is a belief that a woman is sterile while she is nursing and many women prolong the lactation period beyond what is healthful for her or the child, in an effort to stave off another pregnancy. Unfortunately, the method cannot be relied on, and the woman who wants to space her children intelligently should use better methods.

Application of heat to testes

Sperm need a comparatively cool temperature for development. Even body heat is too warm. It has been found that in animals, application of heat to the testicles has induced temporary sterility with no ill effects or loss of potency. However, the sperm already stored in the vas deferens will not be affected. It would require continuous treatment over a period of time to affect a human's fertility. Very little data is available yet on this subject.

Irradiation

X-ray therapy to achieve temporary sterility in the female has been tried on animals. It is not yet known how long the temporary sterility may last nor what permanent danger may ensue, including complete sterility. Such irradiation is now practiced only for other medical reasons. Irradiation of the testes is extremely dangerous and never practiced.

Spermatoxins

Another experimental field. The theory is based on vaccination, where the woman is injected with her husband's sperm, which would set up antibodies *against that particular sperm*. It is still in the laboratory stage.

There remain only the two surest methods to be discussed, sterilization and abstinence. Abstinence is by far the simplest and the least practiced. If you do not have intercourse, you cannot possibly produce a child. Despite its 100% safety, however, it is estimated that it is practiced for that reason by less than 2% of couples. Couples do practice abstinence for brief periods for special reasons, such as ill health or pregnancy, but only very rarely on principle.

Sterilization is the other perfect method. This is recommended only for couples who, for good reasons, must not have children or for those who have had all they can, for various reasons. It is a surgical procedure, simple in the male but more involved in the female, and consists of cutting or tying off the vas deferens or the fallopian tubes.

It does not interfere with potency or sex desire. In some cases, the operation can be reversed and fertility restored. In men, about 25% can be successfully restored, but the percentage is lower in women.

CHAPTER ELEVEN

ABORTION

"Thou shalt not kill".

The Sixth Commandment

Every young married couple look forward eagerly to the time when they will have children of their own. They plan to have each child when they can provide for it and take proper care of it. However, it is not always possible to live according to plan. As we point out in "CONTRACEPTION," it is physically possible for a normal, healthy woman to have more than twenty children during her married life. Carelessness, accident or ignorance of proper safeguards can result in an unwanted pregnancy.

When such a pregnancy occurs, the couple are all too frequently tempted to find some means to terminate. it. Abortion seems an easy way out of the difficulty. IT IS THE WORST POSSIBLE SOLUTION. Death, chronic invalidism, sterility, mental and emotional illness are the price that may be paid. Add to this, the extortionate fees of the abortion racketeers. Yet, in spite of the risks, women are constantly seeking the services of abortionists.

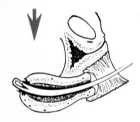

THE DANGER OF ABORTION— AN INSTRUMENT PENETRATED THE WALL OF THE UTERUS

Let us examine the question of abortion in detail. There are two kinds, spontaneous and induced. Spontaneous abortion occurs without outside interference and all too frequently when the parents are anxious for a child. Spontaneous abortion is a medical problem and can be successfully treated by competent physicians with the aid of hormones.

There are two kinds of induced abortion, therapeutic

and criminal. A therapeutic abortion is one which is provided for by law, for the welfare of the mother or the fetus, and is performed by a physician in a hospital, like other operations, with the same care and skill and under the same hygienic conditions. Reasons for therapeutic abortions include such things as: a serious medical threat to the mother due to heart disease, tuberculosis, kidney conditions, cancer, epilepsy, diabetes; an expected abnormal or dead fetus due to the mother having contracted German measles or other virus infections or having taken harmful drugs; severe psychiatric disorders in the mother, such as suicidal tendency, or indications of severe emotional illness resulting from a continued pregnancy; to terminate pregnancies resulting from rape or incest. Because of the existing laws against abortions, physicians are very cautious about performing such operations, and a medical consultation is always called to determine the necessity of the procedure.

In countries where abortions are legalized, there is very little danger since the procedure can be performed at the proper time in the ideal hospital setting. For example, in Hungary, the death rate from abortion performed during the first three months of pregnancy is less than 6 per 100,000.

Criminal abortions are a menace to life and health. The woman seeking illegal medical care is the prey of quacks, charlatans and murderers. This is no exaggeration. To perform an abortion, it is necessary to insert instruments into the uterus and scrape the lining, detaching and removing the fetus. In many cases, the instruments used will perforate the thin wall of the uterus and tear a hole into the abdominal cavity. This nearly always causes death.

Abortion is the chief cause of maternal deaths. Three-quarters of these deaths are due to septicemia, blood-poisoning due to infection. The menace of infection, like uterine perforation, is much greater in criminal cases because these operations are performed, not in hospitals, but doctor's offices, hotel rooms, cubby-hole hideaways, even a midwife's kitchen. Instruments are indifferently sterilized, other materials and surroundings not always clean. The distressed woman seeking aid is in no position to demand hospital hygiene, if, indeed, she realizes its importance.

Frequently, women get off the table, walk several blocks to subway or bus and then ride a public conveyance, perhaps even standing, all the way home. Not having received proper medical advice, the woman may think that since the operation was performed so casually in an office or home, she requires no more care than for a menstrual period. She will try to go about her normal routine, especially if she has a home and children to care for or a job to go to.

If the poor woman survives the operation and is lucky enough to escape septicemia, other perils await her. Women who have had abortions frequently have a much harder subsequent delivery when they finally do have another child. Worse still, a couple who, at one time, resorted to abortion, may discover later that the wife is sterile and they can have no more children. Many female ailments, serious and annoying, have their origin in what seemed, at the time, to be a successful abortion. The interruption of a pregnancy in any way, and especially under the imposed conditions of secrecy, worry, etc., has a depressing and disturbing effect on the nervous and emotional stability of the average woman.

Only too often, the woman seeking abortion is not pregnant at all. It has been estimated that over forty percent of all women coming to the abortionists' offices are not pregnant but are suffering from delayed menstruation. A delayed or missed period is fairly common. There are many physical, emotional and nervous causes for this. Not only serious ailments, but even such a trivial thing as a cold or a quarrel can delay a period. A much stronger deterrent is the fear of pregnancy itself. When a period is delayed, the frightened woman is sure she is pregnant and frequently tries to "do something about it" without first making absolutely certain that she is pregnant. The abortionist does not care and would not tell her the truth. Interested solely in his fee, he goes through the motions of aborting her anyway. If he has enough knowledge to know she is not pregnant, he will merely fuss around and draw blood from the cervix. If the woman has some ailment, this can seriously injure her, while opening the path to infection, in any case. A visit to her own physician, with the making of a pregnancy test, would have relieved her anxiety and saved her from serious danger as well as great expense. The new frog test for pregnancy is considerably cheaper than other tests and infinitely cheaper and safer than abortion or loss of health or life.

Many women pin their faith on medicines. Millions of dollars are hopefully spent every year on drugs purporting to bring about "delayed menstruation", by which the manufacturer intends you to understand "abortion". Only too many women do so understand it. There never was a drug that caused abortion unless there was already a tendency to spontaneous abortion. In which case, the woman probably could not keep the fetus without medical aid even if she wanted to. However, these drugs can cause other troubles, blindness, for instance. Many of them are deadly poisons and others are drastic laxatives. They are excessively expensive, dangerous to use and absolutely worthless for the purpose intended.

Contrary to popular belief and the propaganda of meddlesome "crusaders", at least ninety-five percent of all abortions are performed on married women. The overwhelming majority of these women have several children. It is not that they refuse to bear children, but that they seek relief from too frequent pregnancies. The problems of abortion are enormous. Basically, they are social-economic. This book is not the place for a discussion of such problems. From primitive times, man has tried to devise methods to restrict childbirth. Modern science has finally reached such a high stage in the development of preventive medicine that consultation with your physician and careful application of his advice should greatly reduce the possibility of an unwanted child. If you have economic, psychological or physical problems which would render child-bearing a burden, consult your physician and discuss your problem frankly. If a pregnancy should occur, don't get panicky and do something desperate. Try to replan your family life to include the newcomer and adopt such a frame of mind that when the baby arrives, it will never know, from attitude or action, that it was once unwanted. It will be as welcome as any carefully planned and cherished arrival.

Finally, how does the abortionist, who must work in secret, get his patients? By thoughtless recommendations from one woman to another. If a friend is in trouble, don't recommend some abortionist you may have heard about, thinking you are helping her. You may be helping her to a lifetime of misery, or worse. Give your friend the best advice, the advice you should follow yourself—when in doubt or distress, see your doctor.

CHAPTER TWELVE

VENEREAL DISEASE

CAUSATIVE ORGANISM OF
GONORRHEA

Venereal disease, in its many forms, has long been a source of fear and dread. It was considered a disgrace to contract it, and people went to any length to conceal the fact that they had it. Quacks and patent-medicine manufacturers flourished on the ignorance and shame of victims of the disease. Worse still, people who never had it would spend fortunes getting "cured".

Thanks to the work of various governmental and private health agencies, the public has learned a great deal about venereal disease. They have learned that V. D. is not a disgrace but one of the most wide-spread of human ailments.

CAUSATIVE ORGANISM OF
SYPHILIS

Anyone who has reason to think he may have contracted V. D. should seek medical aid immediately, either from a private physician or one of the many public health clinics. The faster treatment is begun, the better are the prospects of cure. Serious harm can come from delay.

It is not always easy to recognize the earliest symptoms of V. D. Women, especially, may not notice the usual signs. Other symptoms disappear rapidly, which may lull the victim into a false sense of security. That is why it is essential to seek medical help early.

CAUSATIVE ORGANISM OF
CHANCROID

Venereal disease cannot be cured by self-treatment. Only a trained physician can administer the latest techniques that so materially shorten the course of the disease. For instance, early gonorrhea can be cured in twenty-four hours. Syphilis, too, is now treated in record

125

CAUSATIVE ORGANISM OF
GRANULOMA UNGUINALE

time by the latest methods. There are numerous U.S. Public Health Centers throughout the country, and venereal disease clinics in almost every city, where information and help may be obtained free of charge.

For the sake of one's own peace of mind, a doctor should be consulted promptly. If there is no disease present, needless fear and anxiety are averted. No disease was ever cured by worry. It is best to be smart and find out.

ABSTINENCE: To voluntarily refrain from sexual intercourse.

ADRENALS: Two small glands lying on top of the kidneys. Secretions from these glands absolutely necessary to maintain life.

ANATOMY: The structure of the body.

APHRODISIAC: Anything (usually a drug or herb) that is intended to stimulate sex desire.

BARTHOLIN'S GLANDS: Two small glands situated near the opening of the vagina, which exude a lubricating fluid during sexual excitement.

CERVIX: The neck of the uterus. Part that lies within the vagina.

CHROMOSOMES: Microscopic parts of reproductive cell determining sex.

CIRCUMCISION: Removal of the prepuce or foreskin of penis.

CLIMACTERIC: The menopause and corresponding period in the male.

CLITORIS: A small, highly-sensitive organ of erectile tissue located in the vulva (female external genitals). Is reputed to be the seat of pleasure in intercourse.

COITUS: Sexual intercourse.

COITUS INTERRUPTUS: Withdrawal of penis from vagina before climax, during intercourse.

COITUS RESERVATUS: Deliberately prolonging intercourse without reaching a climax.

CONDOM: A skin or rubber sheath for the penis (frequently mispronounced condrum).

CONTRACEPTION: Prevention or avoidance of conception, usually by mechanical or chemical means.

COPULATION: Sexual intercourse.

CORPUS LUTEUM HORMONE: Female hormone essential in pregnancy.

127

DIAPHRAGM: A thin rubber disc used as a contraceptive.

DOUCHE: The cleansing of the vagina by means of a stream of water, usually with added chemicals.

EJACULATION: The expulsion of semen under sexual excitement.

ENDOCRINES: Glands of internal secretion, producing hormones.

ENDOMETRIUM: Lining of the uterus.

EPIDIDYMIS: Tube carrying sperm from testicle (testis).

ERECTION: Fullness and firmness of the genitals from congestion due to sexual excitement.

EROGENIC ZONES: Parts of the body highly responsive to sexual stimulation.

ESTROGEN: The female hormone.

FALLOPIAN TUBES: Tubes carrying the ovum (egg) from ovary to uterus. Site of impregnation.

FERTILE: Prolific, fruitful.

FERTILIZE: To impregnate

FOETUS: The unborn child, between three and nine months.

FRIGIDITY: Female inability to respond to sexual stimulation.

GENES: Part of chromosomes carrying hereditary traits and characteristics.

GLANS: Head of the penis. Most sensitive area.

GONADS: The sex glands. The ovaries in women and testicles (testes) in men.

HORMONES: Chemical substances manufactured by the endocrine glands.

HYGIENE: The science of health.

HYMEN: A fold of mucus membrane partially blocking entrance to vaginal canal.

IMPOTENCE: Lack of sexual power. Failure to achieve erection.

128

INTERCOURSE: Sexual union of male and female, penetration of vagina by penis.

LABIA MAJORA: Outer folds of skin of female genital tract, covered with pubic hair, called outer lips. Part of vulva.

LABIA MINORA: Inner lips of genital tract in female. Part of vulva.

LACTATION: Nursing period following pregnancy.

MEMBRANE: A thin lining in various parts of the body.

MENOPAUSE: End of reproductive cycle of female.

MENSES: Menstruation.

MENSTRUATION: Regular, usually monthly, discharge of blood and other substances from uterus, between puberty and menopause, except during pregnancy.

MUCUS: The secretion of the mucus membrane.

ORGASM: The climax of sexual intercourse.

OVARY: Female sex gland. Producer of eggs (ova), and the estrogenic and corpus luteum hormones.

OVULATION: The discharge of the ripe egg from ovary to fallopian tube.

OVUM: The female egg, or reproductive cell.

PANCREAS: An endocrine gland. In animals, known as sweetbread.

PARA-THYROID: An endocrine gland.

PENIS: The male sex organ.

PINEAL GLAND: An endocrine gland. Connected with sex development.

PITUITARY GLAND: Called the Master Gland. It secretes hormones that control the other hormones and govern all body functions.

POTENCY: Sexual power.

PRENATAL: Before birth

PREPUCE: The foreskin of the penis. Part removed in circumcision.

129

PROSTATE GLAND: Part of male sex apparatus. Secretes fluid that helps propel semen during ejaculation.

PUBERTY: Period when sex awakens in young people.

REPRODUCTION: The begetting of children.

SCROTUM: Pouch of skin containing the testicles.

SECRETION: A substance thrown out by the glands.

SEMEN: Fluid that carries the sperm.

SEMINAL VESICLES: Storage place for sperm. Also secretes seminal fluid.

SMEGMA: Secretion with a foul odor which accumulates under prepuce unless carefully cleaned.

SPERMATOZOA: Sperm, the male seed.

STERILIZATION: Various methods of making either male or female sterile, that is, unable to reproduce, to have children.

SYMPHYSIS: The pubic bone at the front of the pelvis.

TESTICLE: The male sex gland. Also called testis (plural —testes). Producer of male sex hormone, testosterone.

TESTOSTERONE: Male hormone.

THYROID: Large endocrine gland at front of neck.

URETHRA: Canal from bladder. In female, for urination only. In male, seminal fluid is ejected through passage as well as urine.

UTEROSALPINGOGRAPHY: Contrast visualization of the uterus and Fallopian tubes by means of injection of an opaque medium.

UTERUS: The womb, organ where foetus develops.

VAGINA: Canal leading to uterus from vulva.

VAS DEFERENS: Duct carrying sperm from testicles to seminal vesicles.

VULVA: Collective name for external female genitals.